Where Seagulls Cry

by

YVONNE WHITTAL

Harlequin Books

TORONTO • LONDON • NEW YORK • AMSTERDAM • SYDNEY

Original hardcover edition published in 1977
by Mills & Boon Limited

ISBN 0-373-02101-1

Harlequin edition published September 1977

Printed in U.S.A.

For
Doddie Moore

CHAPTER ONE

AUTUMN clouds were drifting across the sky with the promise of rain, while waves lashed the ragged rocks below the cliff with a fierceness that sent the spray several feet into the air. Further along the coast the fishing vessels were pulled high up on to the beach for safety. No one ventured out to sea in this weather lest they should be trapped by gale force winds and tossed about mercilessly by a turbulent sea.

High up on the cliff Kim Harvey stood staring out to sea, the wind whipping her long russet-coloured hair about her face, her hands dug deep into the pockets of her fleece-lined jacket. Leaving Heron's Bay was going to be a wrench, but after Aunt Freda's death there was nothing else she could do other than sell the cottage and move to the city. No one blamed her for this decision as there were very few prospects for a young woman in this small fishing village.

Kim sighed heavily and trudged further up the hill, her comfortable shoes slipping occasionally on the wild grass. There were not many cottages this far up, except for the three or four which were owned by families who used them mainly for holiday purposes. The most isolated cottage was the one on the crest of the hill which had stood vacant for more than a year until someone by the name of Granger had bought it several months ago. Rough steps down the side of the steep cliff led to a private beach where a sturdily built wooden shack housed a motorboat. Apart from this, no one knew much about the owner, except that his car was occasionally seen winding its way up the steep track towards the cottage on the occasional week-end and, like any other small village, the inhabitants were filled with curiosity, and a few unkind speculations.

Dry twigs clung to Kim's slacks and she flicked them off impatiently with her hands. A gust of wind blew her hair across her face once more and, as she straightened to brush the silky strands from her eyes, she saw a man walking slowly and deliberately towards the edge of the cliff. Something more than curiosity made her stop and stare at this tall, lean stranger with the short, but unruly dark hair, his eyes hidden by dark-rimmed sunglasses. His steps were slow and slightly irregular, and quite often he stumbled over the rough surface of the ground as he approached the edge of the cliff.

What the devil was he up to? she wondered when he was barely a few feet from the edge and still showing no sign of stopping. Was he trying to commit suicide?

'What the hell do you think you're doing?' Kim shouted at him frantically, rushing forward on shaky legs and almost stumbling in the process.

'I beg your pardon?'

Kim's anger rose sharply as she stared from him to the edge of the cliff, which was now less than two feet away from him. 'Are you out to get yourself killed, or merely to frighten the life out of me?'

When she had called out to him the first time, he had stopped in his uncertain stride, and now, as he turned towards her, Kim had the curious sensation that he was looking over her head at something beyond.

'I'm blind.'

8

This blunt statement of fact would have shocked most people into a display of contrition and sympathy, but it merely sharpened Kim's anger. 'That's no reason for you to want to kill yourself!' His firmly compressed lips relaxed into a semblance of a smile as they faced each other in silence, but when it appeared that he had no intention of turning back, Kim shrugged her shoulders and turned from him. 'Well, go ahead and take that final step. Throw yourself down on to the rocks and see if I care!'

'Wait!' Kim stopped in her furious stride at the sound of that authoritative voice and, glancing over her shoulder, she saw him extend a hand in her direction as though groping for some kind of support. 'What I am trying to say is that I have no idea how close to the edge I am, and I would be grateful if you would lead me away from it.'

Kim went forward without hesitation and took the extended hand in her own. His fingers curled strong and warm about hers as she led him to safety. 'There's a patch of soft grass further up the hill if you'd like to sit down and rest for a while,' she suggested as she felt him shaking beside her.

'I think I would like that.' His voice was deep and pleasant although slightly clipped with fatigue, while his breath came fast between parted lips.

'You can sit down here,' Kim told him eventually. 'The grass is soft and dry.'

The stranger released her hand and sat down heavily, resting an elbow on his raised knee and burying his face in the crook of his arm. Kim sat down beside him and observed him closely as his breathing became more regular. He was thin, almost gaunt, his clothes fitting loosely on his tall frame. His face was pale and thin, the hollows in his cheeks accentuating cheekbones which would normally not be so prominent. His forehead was broad, and his nose high-bridged and straight, while the firm chin had a slight dent in the centre. It was his hands which finally drew her attention. They were strong hands, despite the slenderness of his fingers, and suggested artistry of some kind. A surgeon perhaps? she wondered curiously.

He raised his head then and there was a grim expression about his mouth. 'Are you sitting down?'

'Yes.'

'I would like to apologise for the inconvenience I've caused you.'

'An explanation would be appreciated more.'

His lips twisted into a tight smile. 'Perhaps I should introduce myself.' He extended a hand in her direction. 'I'm Adam Granger, and you are——?'

'Kim Harvey,' she told him as she clasped his hand briefly.

'Kim,' he repeated softly. 'An unusual name, but I like it. May I call you that?'

'Yes.' So this was the man who had bought that remote cottage, and whom all the villagers were speculating about, she thought as she glanced at him more closely. 'What on earth were you doing walking about unescorted on this treacherous cliff?'

Again that tight smile touched his lips. 'I wanted to go for a walk, and as I'd been here several times before . . . before I was blinded, I thought that I knew in which direction not to go. You could say that I was experimenting towards independence.' A seagull swooped low over their heads and headed towards the beach with a flap of wings, and Adam Granger tilted his head in a listening attitude before he continued. 'I thought that if I counted my steps I would know in future how far I could walk with safety, and I'd counted five hundred and thirty-two when you shouted at me.'

'Well, that's just fine,' Kim remarked sharply, hugging her knees beneath her chin. 'Now you know that you can take five hundred and thirty-three to your death.'

During the ensuing silence between them only the sound of the sea could be heard, while the velocity of the wind increased as storm clouds gathered thickly in the sky.

'Are you always so brutally frank?' he asked suddenly, his mouth relaxing into an unexpected smile that displayed strong, white teeth.

'Always.' Quite unperturbed, she got to her feet and brushed the grass from her slacks. 'Now, if I don't get you home now, we'll both be caught in the storm.'

'Will I be taking you out of your way?'

'Yes, but I don't intend to leave you to wander about aimlessly,' she replied abruptly, taking his hand as he rose to his feet beside her. 'I'll take you home and give whoever is looking after you a piece of my mind for allowing you to go off on your own.'

'You can't blame poor old Solomon,' he remarked as he fell into step beside her, shortening his stride to match her own. 'He had no idea that I would go off on my own, and he's most probably hunting all over the place for me at this moment.'

'Solomon?'

'A black friend I grew up with on the farm,' he

explained. 'My father agreed that he could come and live with me until I manage to sort myself out.'

The first drops of rain splashed into her face when they were still some distance from the cottage. 'Do you think you could hang on to me and run the rest of the way?' she asked.

'I'll try.'

As they approached the cottage the rain increased and Kim guided Adam Granger towards the gate as swiftly as she could. From the opposite direction someone else was making a dash for the cottage and, as he ran towards them, grey-faced and relieved.

'Dr Adam, where have you been? I've been looking all over for you!'

'I went for a walk,' Adam Granger told him calmly. 'I'm sorry if I frightened you, Solomon.'

'As long as you are safe, Dr Adam,' Solomon said with a smile as they dashed inside, 'but you shouldn't go off on your own without telling me.'

'He shouldn't go off on his own at all,' Kim insisted hotly, determined to stress the point.

'The madam is right,' Solomon acknowledged apologetically, wiping the raindrops from his face with the sleeve of his jacket. 'I'll be in the kitchen if you want me, Dr Adam.'

The rain came down in a torrent as they stood in the shelter of the small hallway and Adam Granger appeared to be listening attentively. 'Is it raining very hard, or is that merely the wind?'

'Both,' Kim told him abruptly, shaking the drops of rain from her hair and wondering how she would reach her own cottage without getting soaked to the skin.

'Won't you stay and have tea with me?' he interrupted her thoughts. 'My car is at your disposal and Solomon could drive you down later.'

Kim stood about undecided. A part of her wanted to get away from him as soon as possible, while the other wanted to know more about this man who lived in utter seclusion with only his trusted servant for company.

It was almost as if Adam Granger was aware of her indecision as he moved closer to her. 'Please stay. I could do with some company,' he said persuasively.

'A cup of tea would be most enjoyable at this moment,' she finally relented, staring up into eyes hidden behind those exceptionally dark lenses.

He called down the passage to Solomon, instructing him to make tea before turning to her again. 'The lounge is through here,' he gestured to his right. 'If the room appears rather untidy you must forgive me, but I spend my days here listening to records or just doing nothing.'

The lounge was small with an odd assortment of furniture. Nothing matched, yet nothing jarred, and the visual impact was that of comfortable masculinity. The curtains were a warm wine-red, blending in colour with the stained wooden beams across the ceiling, but her attention was drawn to a bookcase at the other end of the room with rows of impressive-looking books adorning the shelves. Of what use were they to someone who could not see? she wondered with a touch of bitterness. Solomon might be a tremendous help to him, but she was sure that he would be incapable of reading those informative books to his employer.

'Are you a medical doctor?' she asked curiously as she curled up in a chair and glanced at those artistic hands lying limply in his lap.

'No, I'm . . . I was a scientist.'

'Why use the past tense?'

His lips twisted with bitterness. 'I don't think I can be of further use in the scientific field as I am now.'

'That's a defeatist attitude to adopt.'

'Perhaps.' He seemed to be having trouble lighting his pipe and burnt his fingers in the process. Kim watched him with a brooding expression in her green eyes, but did not offer to help him.

'Did you lose your sight quite recently?' she asked.

'Yes.' His pipe was burning properly at last as he dropped the sixth match into the ashtray beside him. 'A month ago, to be exact.'

'How?'

Strangely enough he did not take exception to her probing questions. 'An explosion in one of the laboratories.'

Solomon brought in a tray of tea and placed it on the small coffee table between them. He smiled politely at Kim and then she was once again alone with her strange host. 'Shall I pour?' she asked quite naturally, as if he were quite capable of doing this himself.

'Please do, Kim. I take milk and one teaspoon of sugar.'

The pleasant aroma of pipe tobacco filled the room and Kim was overcome with nostalgia as she poured their tea. Her father always smoked a pipe, and quite often he allowed her to fill the bowl with tobacco for him. It was a little chore she had loved doing despite the fact that her father had grumbled about being capable of doing it himself. Adam Granger laid his pipe aside as Kim took his hand and placed his cup in it.

'I can't understand how anyone in their right mind could have allowed you to come here on your own,' she frowned as they sipped their tea.

'I have Solomon with me,' he replied stubbornly.

'You mentioned something about a farm,' Kim persisted. 'Why didn't you go there where your parents could have helped you through this period of adjustment?'

'After being a widower for several years, my father remarried a little over a year ago.' He emptied his cup and placed it carefully on the coffee table before taking up his pipe once more. 'Libby is a gentle sort of person, but home isn't the same any more; besides, I . . . I'm old enough to take care of myself, don't you think?'

'Well, it's your business really,' Kim shrugged carelessly, 'but I do think you were foolish to come to this isolated place, and next time you decide to take a walk, don't be too proud to take Solomon with you.'

'Yes, ma'am.' His mouth relaxed into a mocking little smile that brought the colour rushing into her cheeks.

Kim judged him to be well in his thirties and, if he were not so thin, he could be devastatingly attractive, she thought irrationally as she placed her empty cup in the tray and rose to her feet. 'I really must go now,' she said.

'I'll tell Solomon to bring the car round to the front,' he said quickly, getting to his feet and walking from the room with practised ease. Kim sauntered across to the window and stared out into the small garden beyond. If Solomon was responsible for the garden, then he certainly made a good job of it. The soil was too poor for a flower garden, but the autumn roses looked magnificent, and the lawns were neatly trimmed. The rain had eased off considerably, Kim noticed, but the wind had not subsided. Adam Granger returned at that moment. 'Solomon won't be long,' he said.

Kim went towards him. 'Well, goodbye, Dr Granger, and thank you for the tea as well as the lift home.'

'Shall I see you again?' There was a touch of eager anticipation in his voice which she chose to ignore.

'I don't think so. I shall be leaving Heron's Bay shortly, and there's so much still to do before I go.'

'Oh.' He resumed his tight-lipped expression. 'Are you on holiday?'

'No, I used to live here with my aunt, but now that she's passed away I'm selling up and moving to the city to find myself a job.'

'I see,' he muttered politely, extending his hand towards her. Kim placed her hand in his and felt again the warm, almost electrifying pressure of his fingers. 'Goodbye, Kim, and thank you for saving my worthless life this afternoon.'

'If you don't shake off your defeatist attitude, your life *will* become worthless,' she told him sharply.

'Kim . . . please come again,' he said unexpectedly, the pressure of his fingers increasing with some urgency. He was lonely, she realised quite suddenly, and in need of company other than the faithful Solomon's. 'To-morrow?'

Kim had the strangest feeling that she should refuse, but this tall, gaunt-looking man had touched a sensitive core in her heart. 'I'll try.'

Kim's meeting with Dr Adam Granger had disturbed her more than she was prepared to admit. The man needed help and encouragement, instead of which he was living a partially isolated life by choice, and quite obviously regretting his decision, judging by his hunger for someone's companionship. She did not want to become involved with him; she could not afford to. If he should come to rely upon her, her eventual departure from Heron's Bay would set him right back to where he was in the first place, and that would be cruel and heartless.

Armed with a hammer and nails, she closed up a crate containing most of her personal possessions. The other things could be sold with the cottage, she decided as she hammered in the nails. Adam Granger's lean face came between her and the crate, and she aimed a vicious blow at the last nail before going through to the kitchen to make herself a cup of tea.

'Kim . . . please come again,' his voice haunted her, and with an angry exclamation she switched on the kettle and stared out through the kitchen window. The wind had subsided during the night, but the rain continued its steady downpour. 'Please come again.'

On the crest of the hill Adam Granger's cottage stood in complete isolation. Her eyes had sought it out on several occasions throughout the morning, and not without a certain amount of guilt. Now, as the afternoon progressed, Kim's guilt overflowed into self-recrimination. She could have paid him a visit earlier in the day. There had been nothing to stop her except her own indecision, and unwarranted reluctance.

She switched off the kettle without waiting for it to boil and hurried from the kitchen. From the hall cupboard she pulled out her raincoat and galoshes, slipping them on before she ventured out into the driving rain. It was a long steep climb up to Adam Granger's cottage, but if she hurried she could be there within fifteen minutes. With her head bent she almost ran up the hill, and not even when his cottage was in sight did she slacken her pace. It was not until her hand was resting on the small wooden gate that she stopped for a moment to catch her breath, her heart pounding in her ears and her cheeks flushed from the exertion. Why this desperate hurry? she wondered to herself as she stepped through the puddles to the front door. She lifted the brass knocker and brought it down sharply before opening the door.

'Hello there!' she called into the silent cottage.

'Kim!' He appeared in the lounge door and came towards her, his hands reaching out and touching her wet raincoat. 'I didn't think you would come.'

She removed her coat and hung it on a peg against the wall before pulling off her galoshes. 'I did say that I would try.'

Adam Granger stood before her, tall and thin in his slacks and sweater and leather jacket. 'I know what you said, but I'm not exactly marvellous company for any young woman as I am.'

'Stop that!' she snapped angrily, the softness of the carpet beneath her feet as she looked up into his lean face. 'Stop feeling sorry for yourself. You're not the only person in the world to have lost his sight.'

There was a deafening silence while he assimilated her surprise attack. 'You're an extraordinary person, Kim Harvey. Your attitude is refreshing, and quite intriguing.' He reached out and miraculously touched her arm with his hand, gripping it tightly. 'Come into the lounge.'

He seated himself in the same chair he had occupied

the previous day, while Kim seated herself opposite him, her bare feet curled in under her. With her slender figure clad in slacks and thick polo-necked sweater, she looked almost boyish, except for her hair which hung straight down on to her shoulders, and which she occasionally flicked away from her face with a small, slender hand.

'I'm glad you came,' he said unexpectedly, and Kim could not prevent the rush of warmth that swept through her, leaving her slightly light-headed.

'Are you, Dr Granger?'

'Yes.' He hesitated briefly, biting his lip. 'I like you, Kim. You don't pity me, or smother me with sympathy. I couldn't stand that.' His taut features relaxed into a smile. 'I'm sure that if I stumbled over something and fell flat on my face, you would tell me, in no uncertain terms, that I should get up and behave myself.'

Kim laughed outright. 'You're most probably right, you know.'

'What is it that makes you so different?'

Russet-coloured hair veiled her face as she lowered her head. 'Perhaps it's because I've had previous experience.'

'I don't think I understand?'

Kim shifted restlessly in her chair. She did not want to talk about herself, but what she had to say might offer some encouragement to this man who found his blindness inacceptable. 'If you feel like listening, I'll tell you a little about myself.'

'I'm listening,' he said, taking out his pipe and lighting it. He was improving, she noticed with a measure of amusement, for he succeeded in lighting it after the fifth match.

'My mother died when I was very young and my father's unmarried sister insisted that we should come and live here with her at Heron's Bay. My father didn't seem to care very much what he did after my mother's death, and besides that, his eyesight was failing and there was absolutely nothing the doctors could do for him.' Kim hesitated a moment and stared hard at the dark lenses hiding his eyes, experiencing the most peculiar desire to know their colour. 'It was my father who taught me so much. He couldn't stand being pitied, and he absolutely hated it when someone showed sympathy. He always maintained that he was not an invalid or a freak, as he called it, and he preferred to be treated like an ordinary person. He was a very astute person, despite his blindness, and there was very little one could hide from him.'

'You speak of him in the past tense,' Adam Granger remarked, sucking thoughtfully at his pipe.

'He died when I was seventeen, and after his death Aunt Freda's health deteriorated rapidly. For the past two years I had to nurse her.' Kim bit her lip to stop its trembling. 'She died last month.'

'I'm sorry.' He clenched his pipe between strong teeth. 'Is there no one else?'

'I have no other family, if that's what you mean,' she replied, recovering her composure and glancing at her watch. It was getting late. 'Shall I make us some tea?'

'Would you?' he half rose in his seat. 'I sent Solomon down to the village to get a few things.'

Kim placed her hands on his shoulders and unceremoniously pushed him back into his chair. 'Stay here and smoke your pipe. If there's something I can't find, I'll call you.'

The kitchen was small but tidy and Kim had no difficulty in finding what she needed. Solomon was either meticulous about putting everything in its proper place, or he had already discovered that a blind person liked to be able to lay his hands on whatever he wanted without having to search for it. Nothing irritated her father more than to discover that something had been removed from its usual place, and the furniture had to remain exactly as it was to allow him to walk about freely in the cottage.

'Do you need any help?' Adam Granger called from the lounge after some time had elapsed.

'No,' she called back, setting the tray. 'With a little more patience you'll have your tea in a moment.'

He was pacing the floor when she entered the lounge, her bare feet making no sound on the polished floor boards. It was as she placed the tray on the table that he turned towards her. 'I get so tired of sitting about,' he complained irritably. 'If the rain would only stop, then I could at least walk about the garden and listen to the seagulls as they fly over.'

He ceased his restless pacing while she poured the tea and sat down once more. 'You shouldn't be here alone,' she said abruptly, placing his cup in his hands. 'You need someone who could talk to you, or read to you. Instead of which you sit here all day brooding about your blindness and becoming your own worst enemy.'

His lips tightened into a thin line. 'Perhaps you're right.'

'I know I'm right,' she told him bluntly. 'And another thing . . . does Solomon cook for you?'

Adam Granger rubbed his chin thoughtfully. 'Well . . . yes. He grills the most delicious meat, and fried eggs are his speciality.'

Kim's green eyes widened in dismay. 'Good heavens, if that's all you ever have to eat then it's no wonder you're so thin!'

'We have sufficient to eat,' he argued stubbornly.

'Probably,' she sighed exasperatedly, 'but you're not eating the right kind of food. It seems to me that both you and Solomon need looking after.'

They drank their tea in silence and Kim wondered nervously what reaction she would get from him. She did not have long to wait, for as he emptied his cup and placed it on the table, he turned slightly towards her.

'You would qualify excellently for the job,' he remarked, his face expressionless.

'I wasn't aware that I was applying.' She faced him tensely, watching the tightening of his lips with a new ache in her heart, and to her own astonishment heard herself saying: 'But if you're serious, and if you think you could bear to have me around, I'll accept.'

Several expressions flitted across his face and Kim watched in fascination as his mouth relaxed into a smile that altered his features entirely. He brushed the thick strands of hair from his forehead, but they fell back again as if they knew no other place to be, and then he leaned forward in his chair. 'Kim, would you really? I don't want to force you to do anything you don't want to.'

His hand was groping towards her and she caught it between her own. 'You will still discover, Dr Granger,

22

that I never say anything I don't mean. As long as you remember that I shall be leaving Heron's Bay within a few weeks.'

His fingers tightened about hers. 'Yes, you did say that you were selling up and moving to the city, but until then I shall be grateful for your company.'

Kim was not sure whether she had done the right thing at all, but she did not have the heart to leave him to his own devices any longer. If no one else cared enough about him to offer assistance, then she would. She could not bluff herself into thinking that she would be intelligent enough to converse with him on his own level, but she would at least be someone to talk to, and someone who could read to him. Once he was able to adapt himself to his blindness, he would no longer need her assistance, or that of anyone else. He could, if he wished, become totally independent, but it would be entirely up to himself.

The rain was still pelting down when she returned home late that afternoon, but there was a certain lightness in her step which had not been there earlier in the day.

CHAPTER TWO

KIM was concerned at first that Solomon might take exception to her presence in the cottage, but his beaming face at meal times soon told her that he thoroughly enjoyed his banishment from the kitchen. Adam Granger seemed to thrive on her cooking as well, for after a week had passed she noticed a definite improvement in his pallor.

'I have a sneaking suspicion that you're trying to fatten me up,' he remarked one afternoon after enjoying one of her dinners.

'You could do with a little more flesh on you.'

'Do I look that awful?'

Kim eyed him critically, ignoring the odd flutter in her heart. 'You don't look awful at all, but I would like to see you grow into your clothes again.'

He took this calmly, acknowledging that he had lost a lot of weight after the accident. 'What's the weather like?' he asked.

Kim glanced through the window. 'There's a clear blue sky and the sun is shining. It's really a marvellously warm autumn day.'

Adam bit his lip. 'Do you think we could go for a walk?'

'Why not?'

With her arm hooked through his, they walked for some distance along the cliff before he spoke, and his voice was tinged with bitterness. 'I used to go down to the beach every morning for a swim, or just to walk along with my feet in the water.' He turned his face towards her and it was difficult to believe that he could not see through those dark lenses. 'Occasionally I went out to sea in my motorboat.'

'I know,' Kim laughed. 'I used to wonder who the reckless fool was who took such chances with a rough sea.'

'I can't think why we never met before,' he remarked, frowning thoughtfully.

'If you'd remained here long enough instead of just coming down on the occasional week-end, you would have found me trespassing on your private beach.' She laughed softly at the look of surprise on his face and flicked her hair across her shoulder in a careless gesture. 'I used to go for a swim or just lie on the beach soaking up the sun. Perhaps the thought that I shouldn't be there made it so much more inviting. Silly, isn't it?'

'Not silly,' he smiled down at her. 'It's understandable and I think I might have done the same.' His face became taut. 'I wish I'd met you then.'

Kim's eyes widened with surprise. 'Why?'

'I would have known what you look like.'

This simple statement sent a stab through her heart, and she thought it better not to linger on the subject. 'Would you like to go down to the beach?' she asked.

He stiffened beside her. 'No, I—I don't think so. The steps——'

'You seem to have no difficulty in going up and down the steps at the cottage, so why not these?'

'What if I stumble and take you down with me?'

'Oh, don't be such a pessimist!' She gripped his arm tighter and led him to the path leading towards the steps. 'There's a safety rail for you to grip as well as my arm, and once you've accomplished it you'll feel enormously better.'

After his initial nervousness he took the dreaded steps in his stride and, as their feet touched the sand below, there was a glow of triumph on his face. 'I wouldn't have been able to do it without you, but it feels good all the same.'

'Of course it does,' she said abruptly. 'Let's take our shoes off and walk along the edge of the water towards those rocks at the furthest end of the beach.'

It was fun walking hand in hand with Adam through the ankle-deep water, with their slacks rolled up to their knees. The seagulls swooped low over them, their plaintive cry as much a part of the sea as the taste of salt on one's lips.

'It's a perfect day,' she told him, automatically reverting back to the days she used to describe everything to her father. 'The sea is a deep blue and perfectly calm as it lies shimmering in the sunlight, with the waves lapping the shore very gently. The sand is so white that it hurts your eyes, and the seagulls are hovering in anticipation above the fishing vessels as they bring their catch home.'

'We can't be far from those rocks now,' he commented.

'No, we're almost there.' Kim glanced at him with swift concern. 'Have I tired you by taking you for such a long walk?'

He pressed her hand reassuringly. 'Stop worrying. I was merely trying to judge the distance for myself.'

Kim found a low rock for them to sit on and for a time they sat in silence, digging their toes into the warm sand and listening to the waves breaking on the shore. Adam's hand, resting beside hers on the smooth rock, moved suddenly as his strong fingers curled about hers. Kim closed her eyes for a moment and remained perfectly still as his thumb stroked the back of her hand, sending unusual little tremors up the length of her arm.

'Your hands are so small and soft,' he said eventually, almost as if he were talking to himself. He reached out suddenly and gripped her shoulders with his hands, turning her towards him. 'What do you look like, Kim?'

'I'm really very ordinary,' she laughed shakily as his hands moved against her shoulders, but she did not move away from him.

'I can't believe that you're ordinary,' he said firmly. 'May I see you my way?'

'You may,' Kim swallowed nervously.

She sat absolutely still as his fingers moved lightly along the column of her throat towards her face. With gentle fingers he explored her forehead, her eyes with their unusually long lashes, her high cheekbones, and her small tip-tilted nose. They lingered for a moment on her quivering lips and then, unexpectedly, he pushed his fingers through her hair and twisted several strands about his hands. Her father had often touched her face and hair like this, but never once had she experienced these peculiar sensations surging through her.

'You're beautiful,' he said at length, his hands still stroking her hair. 'Your hair is so soft and silky. What colour is it?'

'Reddish-brown.' Her words were clipped with the effort of controlling the tremor in her voice. 'And I'm not beautiful, Dr Granger.'

'Adam,' he corrected her. 'Please call me Adam.'

Kim expelled the air from her lungs and obliged. 'Adam, I'm not beautiful. I wouldn't like you to be under a misapprehension.'

'I don't believe you,' he stated bluntly. 'Someone with your character can't be anything but beautiful. What colour are your eyes? Green?'

'Yes.'

'I thought so,' he nodded. 'You're actually rather small.'

Kim laughed then. 'You're actually rather tall.'

Adam smiled suddenly and, as always, it transformed his features into something much less stern. 'My mother always threatened to put a brick on my head if

I didn't stop growing.'

He released her then and she sighed with relief. She could see her own reflection in the dark lenses shading his eyes, and curiosity made her bold. 'Adam . . . will you do something for me?'

He inclined his head towards her without saying anything, but she knew then that he would not object.

'Will you remove those sunglasses just for a moment so that I can see your eyes?'

His lips twitched slightly as if he were amused by something and then he slowly removed his glasses. Kim drew her breath in slowly as she found herself staring into crystal clear blue eyes that seemed to be looking directly into hers as though they were probing deep into her very soul. It was startling, and alarming. His eyes were fringed with dark lashes and if she did not know that he was blind, she would have sworn that he could see her at that moment. He had the kind of eyes that most girls would go crazy about, and even she had to admit that she felt rather weak as she stared into them.

'Well?'

The blood rushed into her cheeks at the sound of amusement in his voice. 'You have very attractive eyes, but perhaps it's just as well that you hide them behind those dark lenses. If you looked at other women the way you're looking at me now, you would have them blushing to the roots of their hair.'

For the first time since she had met him, he threw back his head and laughed heartily. Kim stared at him in absolute fascination. He was a most extraordinary man. 'You should do that more often,' she said.

'What?' he asked, his laughter subsiding as he replaced his sunglasses and turned to her.

'You should laugh more often.' She faced him seriously. 'Do you know, this is the first time I've heard you laugh? Really laugh, I mean?'

'A slight error, my dear Kim,' he smiled blandly. 'An error which shall soon be rectified in your pleasant company.'

'Rubbish!' She turned her gaze towards the sea and frowned at nothing in particular. 'Flattery won't get you anywhere either.'

He took her hand then and pulled her to her feet. 'Very well, Kim, I shan't flatter you in future, but merely speak the truth.' He inclined his head towards her as though he were searching her face. 'The truth is that life has become bearable since I met you, and I wish——'

'Yes?' she prompted curiously.

'Nothing,' he replied bluntly, his lips once again drawn into that firm line which could mean disapproval, anger or bitterness, and Kim was curiously hurt. 'Let's get back to the cottage.'

The situation was becoming increasingly difficult for Kim. As she had feared, Adam had come to rely upon her and he did not hide the fact that he looked forward to her daily visits. In the interim her cottage had been sold, and the new owners were taking possession at the end of that month. That gave her less than three weeks at Heron's Bay, a realisation which caused her concern to grow for Adam Granger. He shunned the idea of going to his father, and seemed strangely reluctant to come to any decision concerning his immediate future. Kim had decided not to force the issue, but now, with

29

so little time left, she would have to make an effort to talk some sense into him.

Adam had not been in a specially good mood lately and his attitude did not exactly offer her much encouragement. Strangely enough it was Adam who brought matters to a head one morning. He accidentally sent his cup of tea crashing to the floor and, after cleaning it up, she calmly poured him another.

'I don't want any,' he said angrily, his lips tightly compressed.

'Now don't be childish,' she snapped back at him. 'Anyone can have an accident.'

He rose to his feet, knocked over a small table, and towered frighteningly above her. 'Stop lecturing me, Kim. I won't have it!'

'Would you prefer it if I pampered your every whim?'

'You know damn well I wouldn't!'

'Well, for goodness' sake, what *do* you want?' she asked despairingly.

The silence grew inordinately long and uncomfortable as she stared up at him. He appeared to be struggling with himself, not quite sure whether he should be angry or remorseful. To Kim's relief his features relaxed, but his whole appearance seemed to droop as he moved about with uncertainty. 'Kim, I'm sorry. I'm bad-tempered lately, but that's no reason why I should take it out on you.'

'If you can't take it out on me, then on who else can you?'

He pushed his fingers through hair that looked as though his fingers had sought refuge there many times before her arrival. 'Now you make me feel a heel.'

'Oh, stop being such a martyr!' she exclaimed,

adopting a ruthless attitude. 'Sit down and let's talk sensibly.'

Adam obeyed reluctantly. 'Kim, I shall miss you when you're gone.' The corners of his mouth curled slightly. 'Who is going to put me in my place when you're not here?'

'That's what I've been wanting to talk to you about,' Kim said determinedly as she left her chair to sit beside him on the couch. 'Have you decided yet what you're going to do?'

'No. I've thought about it constantly, but I still haven't found a satisfactory solution.' He took his time lighting his pipe and Kim let him be as she inhaled the fragrant aroma of the imported tobacco. 'It's time Solomon returned to the farm as well. He's hankering for his wife and kids, and I can't say that I blame him.'

'Have you heard from your father recently?'

Adam nodded, clenching his pipe between his teeth as he spoke. 'He telephoned the other evening, and insisted that I should return to the farm. Libby has apparently been doing some rearranging so that I would have a set of rooms to myself.'

Kim leaned towards him urgently. 'Then why don't you accept, Adam?'

'No!'

There was a desperate finality in his voice that made her flinch with concern. 'But you can't stay here alone. I shall be leaving in a little over two weeks, and you said yourself that Solomon will have to return to the farm shortly.'

'There is, of course, a very simple solution to my problem.'

'And that is?' she asked warily.

He suddenly encountered difficulties with his pipe and laid it aside. 'You could marry me and remain here at Heron's Bay with me.'

Kim's heart leapt into her throat. 'Adam, be serious!'

'But I am!' He turned towards her then with some urgency. 'Look, Kim, think of it as a business arrangement. If at any time you should want your freedom to marry someone else, then I shall give it to you without delay. It is, after all, the only way you can stay here with me without having the entire village in an uproar.'

'And what if you should want to marry someone else?'

'Then the same applies.' He hesitated a moment before continuing. 'Kim, you're the only person I can bear to have around at the moment.'

Kim made a determined effort to gather her scattered wits. 'Marriage isn't something one should contemplate for the sake of convenience,' she stated bluntly, her heart not quite behaving in the usual manner.

'Yes, I know,' he nodded ruefully, but with a hint of mockery. 'A woman wants all the trimmings that go with a marriage, like love and romance.'

Kim stiffened, her temper rising sharply. 'There's no need to sound so pompous about it!'

'Don't tell me you're a romantic at heart?' he asked, surprise and amusement written all over his thin face.

'Yes, I am, and I'm not ashamed to admit it.' Put that in your pipe and smoke it, Dr Adam Granger! she thought angrily.

'There's nothing to stop you from having what you want—eventually—with someone else.'

'With someone else, but not with you,' she thought

wildly, and surprisingly his careless remark hurt. What did he care about her hopes and desires as long as his wishes were complied with? With his clever scientific brain he most probably did not believe in love, but that was no reason why she should discard her views on the subject. Love was something real and wonderful, her father had always told her, and she had seen no reason why she ought not to believe him. She should reject Adam's suggestion outright, she decided firmly, but one look at his anxious face had the power to weaken her resolve.

'But you've only known me for a few weeks, and you don't even know what I look like,' she protested desperately.

Adam smiled openly now. 'I know that you have auburn hair that shines red in the sunlight, and that you were often called Rusty as a child. You have green eyes that darken when you're angry, and sparkle when you're happy. Your voice is pleasant, even when you're bossy, and your laughter reminds me of water rippling down a stream.'

'For goodness' sake——!'

'You're modest and casual, and seldom wear anything other than slacks,' he continued smoothly, ignoring her interruption. 'You stood by your father right up to his death, and after that you did the same for your aunt. You're essentially a giving person, Kim, and the villagers speak highly of you.'

'How—how do you know all this?' she asked with some confusion.

'Some of it you told me yourself, some of it I discovered for myself, and the rest I made it my business to find out.' A flicker of amusement crossed his face.

'You're twenty-two, so I can't be accused of cradle-snatching, and you also blush easily. You're blushing at this moment.'

Her hands flew guiltily to her hot cheeks. 'How do you know?'

'Call it extra-sensory perception if you like,' he laughed, reaching out and removing her hands from her flaming face with alarming accuracy before placing the palms of his own hands against her cheeks. 'You *are* blushing; your cheeks are hot,' he teased, and suddenly his fingers were moving through her hair with some urgency. 'Marry me, Kim. I need you.'

For some moments Kim could not speak or think straight as the touch of his hands sent disturbing sensations racing through her. The absurd desire to feel his lips against her own made her pulse rate quicken, and she crushed the thought instantly. 'Will you . . . give me a little time to consider your proposal?' she asked.

His hands stilled in her hair. 'How much time do you want?'

'I'll give you your answer tomorrow,' she replied shakily as she removed his hands from her hair and escaped to the kitchen to start the dinner.

For the first time, since her Aunt Freda's death, Kim found the loneliness and silence of her cottage oppressive. In the lounge stood a crate, packed and ready for her departure, and beside it stood another, only half full. She stared about her wistfully and allowed the memories to drift back slowly, memories of her father spending many a winter evening sitting by the fireside while she read to him, or merely talked to him quietly.

Aunt Freda was always there, hovering unpretentiously in the background, taking care of their every need. Kim still wondered why her father's only sister had never married. She had questioned her aunt about this several times, but never received a satisfactory reply. Freda Harvey had been more than a mother to her; she had been a friend. She had been warm and loving and giving, making it so easy to give in return, but never expecting anything.

Kim sighed and moved about restlessly. It was past midnight and still she could not sleep. In many respects this had been the most disturbing day of her life. Adam Granger had asked her to marry him. 'I need you,' he had said, and she had promised him an answer the following day. No, that very day, she corrected herself anxiously as she caught sight of the time. With sleep evading her and ample time to think, she still could not make up her mind. What should she do?

It would be a marriage of convenience. A marriage which could be dissolved at the request of either of them, but was this what she really wanted? She recalled the touch of Adam's hands against her cheeks and in her hair, and his face, no longer so painfully thin, barely a few inches from her own. She had wanted him to kiss her, and the recollection brought the familiar heat rushing swiftly into her cheeks, quickening her pulse.

Everything had acquired a quality of unreality after his unexpected proposal that morning. Lunch had been a silent affair as they faced each other across the small table in the kitchen. Afterwards she had read to him for a time from one of his scientific manuals, but when she stumbled over a particularly difficult word for the third time, he had suggested irritably that they should go for a walk. This, too, had not been a success, for their conversation had been stilted and she was, not for the first time, acutely conscious of him as a man, virile and muscular despite his lean appearance.

Kim set aside these disturbing thoughts and went through to the kitchen to warm herself a glass of milk. It was dark and silent outside except for the ever-present sound of the sea lashing the shore. She could not be sure, but it appeared as though there was a light on in Adam's cottage on the crest of the hill. Was he, too, finding it difficult to sleep? She tightened the cord of her gown and turned just in time to prevent the milk from boiling over on to the stove. With trembling hands she filled a glass and took it upstairs with her, turning out the lights as she went.

Sitting up in bed sipping the warm milk, she seriously considered Adam's proposal once more. 'Marry me, Kim. I need you,' his words kept winding their way through her thoughts, and she felt again the stirring of her emotions when his hands had moved so gently through her hair.

'What is love? How shall I know it if I should encounter it?' she had once asked her father. 'You will know without being told,' he had replied, smiling gently as if recalling his own experiences. 'When strange things start happening to you at a certain look, or the touch of a hand, then you'll know that you've come face to face with love.' Kim had not quite believed this at the time, but now?

She gulped down the rest of her milk and reached out to snap off the light before she snuggled down beneath the blankets. Adam Granger! What was there about the man that disturbed her so? He was tall and lean, and since she had seen to it that he had regular, nourishing meals, his clothes no longer hung limply on his frame. His short dark hair was unruly and always fell untidily across his broad forehead, and there was strength in his hands as well as gentleness. Had she not experienced their gentleness as they touched her face, her hair?

Kim's breath came rapidly over parted lips. This was absurd, she told herself sternly as she struggled to still the heavy beating of her heart. She had looked into his eyes only once, her relentless thoughts continued, and even then she had experienced a drowning sensation and an electrifying magnetism in their startling blue depths. He needed her, he had said. Was it only because of his blindness? If, by some miracle, he regained his sight, would he still need her, or would he discard her like some object which had served its purpose?

Kim moaned softly into the darkness and buried her face in the pillow. It was useless trying to escape the truth. She loved Adam Granger, and would do anything to make him happy. What did it matter that he scoffed at love? She loved him! Perhaps, in time, he might learn to care for her in his own peculiar fashion, but until then it was sufficient to know that he needed her. Marriage to Adam, she decided eventually, was something worth risking. It was a risk that would require endless patience if she wanted their marriage to be a success, but it could also very easily break her heart.

Kim stopped for a moment to catch her breath before attempting the last few yards to Adam's cottage. There was nothing elaborate about his temporary home, which had originally been bought with the intention of only spending week-ends and holidays there. The garden was small and neat, the lawn beautifully green after the recent rain, with a splash of colour from the roses ranking up the one wall. Geraniums flowered in the window-boxes and the birds seemed to find this quite intriguing. Adam's cottage was not very large. It had a lounge, kitchen and dining-room downstairs, but Adam preferred eating in the kitchen. It was less trouble and more cosy, he had remarked once. Upstairs there were two bedrooms and a bathroom, and a smaller room which he used as a store-room. In the back yard stood a rondavel which Solomon had cleaned out to use as his sleeping quarters. She supposed that Solomon would return to the farm as soon as she and Adam were married. Kim blushed profusely at her own presumptuous thoughts. They were not married yet, and besides that, it was really none of her business.

To her surprise it was Solomon who met her at the gate, and his expression relayed relief as well as concern. 'I'm glad the madam has come,' he stated promptly.

'Is there something the matter?' she asked, fear clutching at her heart.

'Nothing serious, madam.' He shook his head. 'The madam must be careful this morning. Dr Adam has got the devil on his back.'

'Has he, indeed?' Relief bubbled into laughter which she swallowed swiftly as she adopted a serious attitude to match his own. 'What's troubling him?'

'I don't know, madam. All I know is that he wouldn't eat his breakfast this morning, and he is throwing the furniture about in the lounge.'

38

'Oh, dear!'

'If anyone can calm him down, then the madam can,' Solomon continued with a confidence that was touching. 'I'll be here in the garden if the madam should want me.'

Kim could not suppress the nervous little shiver that went through her as she entered the cottage. Adam was pacing the lounge floor and, by the sight of the small tables lying scattered across the room, having a wonderful time kicking everything out of his way. A smile lurked in the green depths of her eyes and lifted the corners of her mouth. So Adam had a temper, it seemed.

'Good morning, Adam.'

He turned on her and without the dark lenses which normally shaded his eyes, he looked anything but blind as his gaze appeared to burn through her scornfully. 'Well, you certainly took your time getting here this morning,' he snapped harshly, and quite obviously in a filthy temper.

'Don't be silly, it's only just after eight,' she retaliated as she approached him, 'and I would say good morning first, if I were you.'

'What's good about it?' he demanded irritably, not attempting to move about in her presence. 'For all I know it could be snowing outside.'

Kim flung her handbag into a chair and removed her jacket. In her neatly pressed beige slacks and white woollen jersey she looked as innocent as a child with her hair hanging straight down on to her shoulders, and her cheeks still flushed from the exertion of trudging up the hill. 'It isn't snowing,' she told him briskly, 'the sun is shining.'

'The wind is blowing.'

'It's just a light south-easterly breeze,' she contradicted.

'It howled all night long and I hardly slept a wink,' he continued stubbornly.

'It never howled all night and, for your information, neither did I have a very good night, but I'm not complaining.'

Kim hated having to talk to him so sharply, but to sympathise with him at a time like this would only serve to increase his agitation. There was only one way to get him out of this mood, and that was to bully him verbally; to match his temper with her own. The proof of her success was in the glimmer of a smile that lurked in his eyes; eyes that had a great deal to do with the peculiar weakness in her knees.

'I've a feeling that if I told you the devil was standing in that doorway, you would argue and say that it was an angel with horns on its head.'

'But the devil *was* an angel of God,' she replied swiftly.

'Oh, Kim, I can't win, can I?'

He seemed so pathetically helpless, and so very dear, that she almost weakened. 'Not when you're deliberately trying to be difficult.'

'Difficult?' he demanded as a last gesture of defiance. 'Who's being difficult?'

'You are.'

'Now see here——'

He got no further, for Kim's helpless laughter rang in his ears and banished any further desire of displaying temperament. 'You're laughing at me,' he accused.

'Not at you,' she corrected, making an effort to control herself. 'At us.'

'What's so funny?' he demanded suspiciously.

'You are. I am,' she told him promptly, taking his hands and pulling him down beside her on the couch. 'You asked me to marry you yesterday and as a result neither of us slept very well last night.'

'I'm glad to hear that you at least remembered that I'd proposed to you,' he remarked sullenly.

'A proposal isn't something a girl forgets easily,' she admitted freely. 'It took time, though, coming to some sort of decision.'

'And?'

His hands moved upwards along her arms to her shoulders and Kim kept a tight rein on her quivering emotions. 'If you are still sure that you want to marry me, then my answer is . . . yes.'

She could not explain afterwards how it had happened, but quite suddenly his hard mouth had taken possession of hers and she could not recall any desire on her part to struggle for release. His action had been swift and unexpected, and although every nerve in her body tingled in response, he appeared quite unaffected when he released her after what seemed like endless seconds.

'Thank you, Kim,' he said quietly and with a new calmness. 'I shan't let you regret this decision of yours.'

CHAPTER THREE

ADAM wasted no time in getting the local clergyman to pay them a visit, and Kim had a faint suspicion that he had no intention of giving her time for second thoughts. The Reverend Mr Wilson needed no introduction to Kim, for he had been at Heron's Bay ever since she could remember. When they heard his car stop outside the gate, Kim glanced at Adam with a certain amount of amusement as he searched his jacket pockets for his sunglasses.

'I hate the thought of not being able to look people in the eyes,' he explained tersely as he put them on. 'I always have that sinking feeling that I'm looking beyond them, and this way I can at least pretend to be looking directly at the person to whom I'm speaking.'

'You've been doing nothing but look directly at me ever since I arrived this morning,' she laughed nervously, biting her lip. 'It's most unnerving.'

'That's because you have such a vibrant personality,' he remarked, half in jest and half in ernest. 'I always know exactly where you're standing, or sitting.'

'Do I take that as a compliment, I wonder?' Kim laughed, but there was no time for Adam to reply, for Mr Wilson was already knocking firmly on the front door.

'Let him in, Kim,' Adam instructed, lighting his pipe as he remained seated.

She hastened to the door and admitted Mr Wilson. 'Kim, it is good to see you,' he smiled broadly, the sun glistening on his bald head. 'I must admit, my dear, that the reason for this visit is rather unexpected. I had no idea that you knew Dr Granger so well.'

Kim nervously acknowledged his greeting, but was unable to find an adequate reply to satisfy his curiosity. 'Would you come this way? Adam is waiting in the lounge.'

She ushered Mr Wilson into the lounge and he shook hands with Adam in his usual pleasant manner before he lowered his rather stout figure into one of the armchairs. An awkward silence seemed to settle in the room as Kim glanced from Adam's taut face to Mr Wilson's calm but openly curious features.

'Shall I make a pot of tea?' she asked, her voice sounding unnatural to her own ears.

'Perhaps that will be a good idea, Kim,' Mr Wilson agreed, clearing his throat. 'I don't think we particularly need you at the moment, and Dr. Granger could quite easily give me the necessary information.'

Kim escaped to the kitchen without hesitation, taking longer over the tea than was absolutely necessary. How long did it take to arrange a marriage? she wondered nervously, wiping the cups for the second time. She could still hear the low rumble of their voices in the lounge, and waited just a few minutes longer before taking the tray through.

'Ah, here's the bride-to-be,' Mr Wilson smiled as she entered the room, and Kim nearly dropped the tray. 'Everything is arranged for next Saturday—that's in ten days' time. I must say that Dr. Granger doesn't like wasting time once he has decided on something,' he went on smoothly as Kim handed him his tea.

'Have you—is everything arranged?' Kim glanced at

43

Adam as she placed his cup of tea in his hand, but his expression was completely uninformative.

'Everything is arranged, Kim,' he told her quietly. 'Under the circumstances it will be a quiet wedding with only my parents present. It's as we decided.'

'Dr Granger has also agreed that my wife take a few photographs on the occasion,' Mr Wilson added. 'She's the only one with proper photographic equipment in the village.'

Kim's heart raced at a suffocating speed. 'Yes. Yes, of course.'

A photograph of Adam and herself on their wedding day! A visual reminder of a marriage arranged for the sake of convenience!

Adam remained tense for the rest of Mr Wilson's visit and, as if sensing their desire to be left alone, the fatherly clergyman did not delay his departure longer than necessary. Kim followed him outside to his car in silence, her nerves tightening into a ball at the pit of her stomach at the sight of his deepening frown.

'Kim, I'm glad that we have these few moments alone,' he began as they reached the gate. 'I feel that, in the absence of your father and your aunt, it's my duty to speak to you as they would have done.'

'Mr Wilson, I——'

'Wait!' he interrupted her swiftly with a silencing gesture of his hand. 'I've known you since you were a little girl, and I've seen your loyalty to those closest to you. I have nothing against Dr Granger, but I must ask you a few questions.'

Kim met his steady glance and knew that there would be no escape. 'Very well,' she sighed. 'What do you want to know?'

'How long have you known Dr Granger?'

'A few weeks.'

'In fact, not more than a month, for that is how long he has been here at Heron's Bay. Is this not so?'

'Yes.' Kim lowered her glance and felt the colour stain her cheeks.

'I'm well aware of your tender heart, Kim,' he went on gently, 'but aren't you letting the fact that he's blind influence you in any way?'

Kim met his glance once more and there was no mistaking the determination in the set of her small chin. 'What you actually want to know is, am I not allowing Dr Granger to take the place of my father because they had blindness in common?'

Mr Wilson cleared his throat self-consciously. 'Something like that, yes.'

Kim shook her head. 'No, Mr Wilson, I'm not.'

'Are you quite sure that what you feel for him is love, and not pity?'

Kim directed her gaze beyond the cliff to where the sea met the sky and, for a moment, she was completely alone with her thoughts. Is pity and compassion not a part of love just as the earth is part of the universe? She loved Adam, of that she was sure, and because she loved him she felt pity and compassion for him, but she would not have contemplated marrying him merely out of pity alone. No, her reason for accepting his proposal went far deeper than that, and far beyond the range of compassion.

The touch of a hand on her arm brought her attention back to the present, and Mr Wilson's look of concern. 'Kim, I ask you again. Do you love him?'

'Yes, I do,' she replied with conviction.

The frown relaxed slightly above the bushy eyebrows. 'Does he love you?'

'He needs me,' the words were torn from her as she struggled to control the trembling of her lips. 'Don't be concerned for me, Mr Wilson. I'm going into this marriage without any illusions.'

His hand moved to her shoulder in a comforting gesture. 'God bless you, my child.'

Kim stood for quite some time watching him drive slowly down the hill before she turned towards the cottage, brushing the tears from her eyes with the tips of her fingers before entering.

'Well?' Adam's lips twisted with a touch of cynicism.

'Well, what?' she demanded abruptly, gathering up the tea things and placing them on the tray.

'Did he try and talk you out of it?'

The tea cups rattled as Kim brought the tray down heavily on to the table. 'Yes, he did.'

A tense silence settled between them as she searched those sightless blue eyes for some indication as to his feelings. 'I appreciate your honesty,' he said at last, his lips drawn into a thin line of disapproval. 'Did he succeed?'

She went towards him then, taking hold of his hands as she sat down beside him. 'I gave you my word that I would marry you, and once I've given my word I never take it back.'

Adam's stern mouth relaxed slightly. 'If you hadn't given your word to me, would you still have gone through with the marriage after having a talk with Mr Wilson?'

Kim was perilously close to admitting the truth, but she smothered the desire instantly. 'Even if I hadn't given my word, I would still go through with it.'

'Why?'

'You did say that you needed me,' she replied carefully. 'A woman sometimes likes to be needed.'

Again that tense little silence followed. 'Are you sure that you're not marrying me because you pity me?'

There it was again, that word her father had hated so much. Pity! Mr Wilson had asked her the same question and she had at least been able to give him a truthful answer, but what reply could she give Adam? What could she say?

'I don't pity you, Adam,' she said eventually with a fierceness that hid her turbulent emotions. 'I'm marrying you because you're such an irritable, bad-tempered, pigheaded sort of person, and I enjoy sparring with you.'

'Well,' he laughed suddenly, 'that's something quite unique which should go down in the annals of history! I don't think anyone has ever offered those reasons for contemplating marriage.'

'I don't think many women have found themselves in the position I'm in at the moment,' Kim added bluntly, releasing his hands and getting to her feet. 'Your reasons for proposing are just as unique as my reasons for accepting.'

'Perhaps you're right,' he agreed, and she had the impression that he was tired of the trend the conversation was taking.

'I have to see to lunch,' she mumbled, but, as his dark head went down against the back rest of the couch, she hesitated curiously. 'How old are you, Adam?'

An odd smile flickered across his face. 'Thirty-five. Does that sound ancient to you?'

'Don't be silly!' she muttered angrily, scooping up

the tray and escaping from that blue gaze that continually threatened to turn her knees to water.

The ten days before the wedding passed with alarming swiftness for Kim. She had so much to do, and so much still to be done, that she hardly ever had time to brood about the decision she had made. Solomon seemed inordinately thrilled at the idea that he would soon be returning to his family, but Adam surprised Kim most of all. He remained calm and unruffled despite the fact that his home was in complete disruption.

Mrs Wilson insisted that Kim slept at the manse the last night before the wedding, and it was arranged that Mr Wilson would call for her at Adam's cottage that afternoon. Henry and Libby Granger arrived that same afternoon in their small truck as Adam had asked them to, and Kim, after her initial nervousness, found them extremely likeable. Henry Granger, tall but not as lean as Adam, seemed not at all surprised at his son's sudden decision to settle down, whereas his wife, Libby, asked curious questions which often embarrassed Kim.

Kim was thankful when Mr Wilson finally arrived to collect her, but Adam was not letting her go that easily.

'Would you all mind leaving Kim and me alone for a few minutes?' he asked courteously, and three astonished people trooped from the lounge and closed the door firmly behind them.

'Give me your hands,' he said, coming towards her, and she placed her hands nervously in his as she stared up into those unseeing blue eyes. 'Kim, this is your last chance to change your mind if you have any doubts.'

She drew a quivering breath and wished at that moment she could fling herself into his arms. 'I have no doubts, Adam. Have you?'

'No.' His hands moved upwards along her arms to eventually circle her face. 'I just wish it was all over so that we could be alone again. All these people around me make me nervous.'

'You haven't looked nervous at all,' she laughed shakily. 'I was beginning to think you were completely unaffected by it all.'

A smile hovered on his lips. 'You wouldn't say that if you knew how my stomach seems to have twisted itself into a permanent knot.' He dropped a light kiss on to her hair and moved away from her. 'Kim, I've told Solomon to take my father's truck and follow Mr Wilson's car down to your cottage. He'll load up those two crates you spoke of, and anything else you want to have brought up here.'

'Thank you, Adam.'

The murmur of voices outside the door made them realise that they could not continue their conversation at the expense of others, and Adam gestured that she could open the door.

Nothing seemed entirely real after that. Mr Wilson drove her down to her cottage with Solomon following closely in the truck. They loaded the two crates on to the truck as well as a few suitcases of clothing she would not be needing immediately, and after Solomon's departure she had only her wedding dress and a suitcase containing a change of clothing to take with her. There was no time to feel any nostalgia as she locked the door of her cottage behind her for the last time. This been her home for so many years, and yet she could not conjure up a twinge of regret at that final moment of parting with the familiar. Tomorrow she would be marrying Adam, and that was enough to occupy every part of her mind and soul.

Mr Wilson very kindly drove Kim to the estate agents to hand in the key before taking her to the manse where Mrs Wilson awaited them to show Kim up to the room she had prepared for her.

'Mrs Wilson, it's exceptionally kind of you to put me up for the night——' Kim began, but Mrs Wilson brushed aside her words of thanks.

'Freda Harvey would never forgive me, had she been alive, if I'd allowed you to remain all alone in that empty cottage on the eve of your wedding,' she explained with a warm smile.

After the mad rush of the past ten days, the peaceful atmosphere of the manse and its people had a soothing effect on Kim's nerves, and she slept soundly that night, to be awakened on her wedding day with the sun streaming in through the window.

The wedding was scheduled for ten o'clock that morning to enable Adam's parents to return to their farm immediately after lunch and, with only two bedrooms in Adam's cottage, this was an ideal arrangement for both of them. Kim did not linger in bed on that perfect April morning. Adam had said that they would arrive at the manse half an hour before the wedding, so that did not leave her much time to laze about. She had a quick bath and returned to her room immediately after breakfast to change and pack the few personal possessions she had brought with her.

Her wedding day became a reality as she stared at herself in the mirror, but, strangely enough, it did not unnerve her. Her wedding gown, which had cost her a trip to Cape Town by train besides the unearthly price she had had to pay for the dress, was of a soft white satin that accentuated her youthful slenderness. All this for Adam, and he would not be able to see her, she thought sadly, but perhaps it was just as well. Let him continue imagining that she was attractive when, in reality, she was really rather plain. What difference did it make what she looked like, as long as Adam thought her attractive, and it was, after all, a marriage of convenience. She winced inwardly as she placed the shoulder-length veil on her head, securing it with a hairpin.

Mrs Wilson knocked at the door and entered. 'Dr Granger and his parents have arrived,' she said with a smile, and then stopped for a moment to stare at Kim. 'My dear, I've never seen you look so lovely.'

'It's very kind of you to want to boost my ego,' Kim thanked her dully, 'but I'm afraid that Adam has found himself a rather plain wife.'

'Don't be silly!' Mrs Wilson exclaimed, shocked at Kim's description of herself. 'Take another look at yourself in the mirror. I've always envied you your glorious hair and those remarkable eyes. Did you know that they change colour with your moods?' Kim laughed shakily at this, but Mrs Wilson continued undeterred. 'They do, you know. There's character and quality in your face that isn't always easy to find in others.' She leaned confidentially towards Kim and whispered, 'As a clergyman's wife, I'm not supposed to say this, but, with a little touch of make-up, you could be very attractive.'

Kim's eyes widened. 'Do you think so?'

'Just you wait here.' Mrs Wilson disappeared and returned a few moments later with a small wooden box in her hands. 'I keep it hidden from Albert,' she laughed mischievously, 'or he might just decide one day to get rid of my secret weapons.'

'Oh, Mrs Wilson, you're wonderful!' Kim laughed outright.

Mrs Wilson was right. With a light cream base and a touch of powder and lipstick there was a remarkable improvement in her appearance. Staring at her reflection in the mirror at that moment, she could almost call herself attractive, she thought humorously.

'We mustn't keep the groom waiting any longer,' Mrs Wilson interrupted her thoughts and, taking Kim's suitcase, she led the way downstairs to the living-room.

Kim stopped in the doorway and stared in astonishment at the man she was about to marry. This was a new Adam she had not met before. His dark hair was brushed back severely from his forehead and in his dark suit and matching tie he looked exceedingly attractive. The whiteness of his shirt contrasted drastically with his tanned complexion and in his tailored outfit he displayed a muscular leanness which had been hidden beneath the baggy sweaters and comfortable slacks he always wore. She drew her breath in sharply. It was almost as though she were marrying a stranger, she thought nervously.

'Kim?' he said, an edge of uncertainty in his voice, and suddenly she was oblivious of everyone else in the room except Adam and herself.

'I'm here, Adam.' She went towards him swiftly, taking the hands he held extended towards her.

A familiar smile curved his usually stern lips. 'I thought for a moment that you were contemplating escape.'

She looked up into his face, the dark lenses hiding his expression from her. 'I told you once before that once I've given my word, nothing would make me withdraw it.'

The pressure of his hands tightened on hers. 'I wish I could see you at this moment.'

His words touched her heart with aching precision and for a moment she could not speak for fear of crying.

'Kim is a vision of loveliness,' Libby said swiftly, and this was echoed by everyone else. Even Mr Wilson coughed and grunted something complementary.

'What are you wearing, Kim?' Adam asked unexpectedly, and Kim glanced appealingly at Mrs Wilson, only to discern from her gesture that this was Kim's department entirely.

Kim glanced up at Adam's expectant face above hers and swallowed nervously. 'My dress is m-made of s-satin material, long-waisted with a ballerina-length skirt,' the words came out in a rush. 'Tiny beads have been embroidered very effectively around the neckline, and because this is autumn I thought that it would be safe to choose a dress with three-quarter-length sleeves.'

'Are you wearing a veil?' he asked after a moment, as if he were endeavouring to form a picture of her in his mind.

'Yes,' Kim replied nervously. 'A shoulder-length veil fastened on my head with orange blossom.'

'What colour?'

Kim's heart hammered heavily against her ribs. 'Do —do you mean my dress?'

'Naturally.'

Kim could not suppress the shiver of anxiety that

went through her. 'White.'

The silence was tense in the manse's living-room until Adam's features relaxed into a smile of pleasure. 'I'm glad,' was all he said, but it was enough to bring the colour back to Kim's pale cheeks.

Mr Wilson cleared his throat. 'I don't want to rush the two of you, but it's almost ten. Shall we go along to the church?'

It was a silent group of people that followed Mr Wilson through the gate dividing the church from the manse, but as they entered the church moments later, Kim stopped suddenly in her stride.

'Wait!' She glanced up at Adam's startled face and said with her usual impulsive candour, 'I refuse to marry you, Adam, unless I can see your eyes.'

An audible sigh of relief escaped him as he reached up to remove the offending sunglasses. 'Is that better?'

'Much better,' she replied, losing herself for a moment in those blue depths as he met her gaze directly. At times like this it was almost impossible to believe that he could not see directly into her soul.

Mr Wilson cleared his throat impatiently and they continued the long walk down the aisle. At Adam's request it was not a lengthy ceremony. At the appropriate moment he placed the plain gold band on Kim's finger without fumbling for one second and, after the blessing had been bestowed upon them, Mr Wilson announced from the pulpit that Adam might kiss his bride.

In absolute silence Adam took her face between his hands and lowered his head, his lips claiming hers in a kiss so unspeakably tender that it brought tears to her eyes. Surely, after such a display of tenderness on his part, he would not find it difficult to care for her eventually? She closed her eyes for a brief moment and sent up a silent prayer.

She sat beside Adam in the back of his Peugeot as they drove to his cottage, and somehow his hand found hers on the seat between them. Her fingers curled involuntarily about his and her heart leapt as she felt the answering pressure of his.

'We're almost there,' Libby said from the front seat beside her husband. 'I hope you don't mind, Kim, but under the circumstances I thought it best to prepare a cold lunch.'

'Don't forget the bottle of champagne in the fridge,' Henry added. 'It's going to be a celebration dinner.'

'It sounds delightful,' Kim assured them, glancing at Adam for confirmation, but he merely stared straight ahead as though he were totally uninterested.

Henry Granger drew Kim aside shortly before their departure from Heron's Bay that afternoon to express his relief that Adam had not allowed his blindness to prevent him from leading a normal life. If only he knew! Kim thought sadly.

'Adam must return to his work eventually,' Henry continued, his lean face, so like Adam's, showing extreme concern. 'He can't spend the rest of his life just sitting around, so you'll have to work on him.'

'I don't think Adam would appreciate being bullied into anything, Mr Granger,' Kim told him seriously. 'He will pick up the threads of his former life when he's mentally ready to face it, and I shall naturally encourage him in that direction.'

'Good girl,' he smiled happily.

Kim stood beside Adam as his father and stepmother

took their leave. Solomon was the first to say goodbye before he climbed on to the back of the truck with his shabby suitcase and blankets. He smiled broadly at the prospect of seeing his family again and Adam, as if he sensed Solomon's excitement, teased him a little.

'Take good care of yourselves,' Henry and Libby said as they climbed into the truck, waving for the last time as it gathered speed down the hill.

'Thank goodness they've gone,' Adam sighed as they re-entered the cottage. Kim echoed this but maintained a nervous silence.

They were now alone, completely alone, she thought as she stood about nervously, twisting the unfamiliar ring about her finger. Adam slumped on to the couch and loosened his tie. The tired lines about his mouth were suddenly more pronounced, she noticed and, forgetting her own nervousness, she went to his side with swift concern.

'Are you tired? Would you like a cup of tea now, or would you prefer to go up and change first?'

A smile of tolerant amusement curved his lips. 'You're the only person I've ever met who can punch out several questions in rapid succession without taking a breath.'

Kim coloured profusely. 'I'm sorry.' She swallowed convulsively. 'Now that it's all over I'm as nervous as a kitten.'

'Honest Kim,' he remarked with a certain grimness, reaching for her hand and pulling her down beside him. 'That's what I like about you. You're always so damned honest.'

'Would you prefer me not to be?'

His heavy eyebrows rose sharply. 'Good heavens,

56

no! You're the one person I can trust to always tell me the unvarnished truth. Don't ever change, Kim.'

His voice was low, almost pleading and, without thinking, Kim raised his hand to her lips. 'I shall never lie to you, Adam, if that's what you want.'

His expression altered swiftly, becoming strangely aloof. 'The absolute truth between us always?'

'Yes, Adam. Always,' she whispered, and at that moment her heart was in her eyes, laid bare for all to see but Adam.

There was a profound silence between them that made her wonder whether she had gone too far. Was she expecting too much from Adam to demand complete honesty from him in return? She chewed her bottom lip nervously and wondered miserably just what was expected of her.

'What were those questions you rattled off a moment ago?' Adam asked eventually, unaware of the storm of uncertainty which shook Kim.

'I asked if you were tired,' Kim repeated self-consciously.

'A little,' he admitted, releasing her hand, 'and I think I *will* go up and change while you make us a pot of tea.'

It was some time later that afternoon, after Kim herself had changed into her usual slacks and sweater, that Adam helped her unpack the crate of linen on the back porch. The second crate, with an odd assortment of books and earthenware, had been stored away in the rondavel which Solomon had occupied. The suitcases containing her clothes had been placed in the room Adam's parents had occupied. As it was the only room with a double bed, it was naturally assumed that Adam would move in there with her. Kim coloured at the thought but mentioned nothing of this to Adam. The bedrooms, just like the lounge, contained odd pieces of furniture, some of which Adam had taken over from the previous owners while the others had been bought at random.

With her linen stored away in the linen cupboard beneath the stairs, Kim began to unpack her suitcases.

'If you need any help with that, just call,' Adam had teased, and she had assured him blushingly that his help was not needed. 'It was just a suggestion,' he added, grinning broadly and looking more boyish than she had ever seen him.

It was a strange new experience being at the cottage with him after dark, and Adam seemed to find immense enjoyment in her presence. He refused to remain in the lounge on his own and stood about the kitchen while she made them omelettes for supper. Neither of them were very hungry after the extravagant meal his step-mother had prepared, but Kim insisted that they should eat something.

'I think a bottle of champagne has been left in the fridge,' Adam said eventually. 'Shall we open it and have it with our supper?'

Kim giggled profusely. 'What a combination! Omelettes and champagne!'

'At least it's quite original,' Adam remarked with his back to her as he opened the fridge and found the bottle without much trouble. He removed the silver wrapping around the top and began to ease off the cork. 'Have some glasses ready so that you can pour.'

It turned out to be a memorable occasion. Kim, un-accustomed to the large quantities of champagne she had consumed that day, continually had to suppress the helpless giggles that struggled to the fore. Adam, too, was not unaffected, for she encountered a lighthearted side to his nature she had never seen before. It appeared that there were many sides to this man she had married, and discovering each phase was going to be a new delight.

They parted company at the door to his room later that night and Kim entered the lonely isolation of her own. This was her wedding night, and she was spending it alone. The enormous double bed with its iron posters offered little comfort as she rolled about in the dark, listening to the sound of the sea lashing the rocks below the cliff. It was strange that it could be heard so much clearer from Adam's cottage. She had always been aware of the sea at her aunt's cottage, but somehow from this high vantage point it could be heard so much clearer. It was, however, a soothing sound, but Kim was too restless to be soothed. Was Adam asleep? she wondered eventually, considering a trip to the kitchen to warm some milk. She tried once more to sleep, but finally gave up the struggle and slipped out of bed and put on her gown and slippers.

Adam was still awake; the strip of light beneath his door told her so. It was strange, this phobia of his to have the lights on despite his blindness, or perhaps it was merely a display of keeping things as normal as possible. Kim hesitated outside his door for a moment and then, hearing his footsteps moving about, she knocked and opened the door slightly.

'Adam? Are you decent?'

'Yes,' he laughed shortly. 'Come in.'

She went in then and found him standing in the centre of the floor in his pyjamas and dressing gown.

His bed showed signs of his struggle for sleep, but otherwise there was no sign of disorder in the room.

'I couldn't sleep,' she explained nervously. 'It must be the tension and the champagne.' Adam's lips curved into a mocking smile and she blushed profusely. 'I'm going to warm myself some milk, would you like some as well?'

'Yes, I'll come with you.'

This surprised her, but she maintained a stony silence as they went downstairs to the kitchen. She poured the milk into a saucepan and placed it on the stove while Adam pulled out a chair and sat down with his arms resting on the table.

'It's been a rather strenuous day for both of us,' he remarked understandingly. 'I found myself too keyed up to sleep as well.'

Kim remained silent, unable to think of anything to say. What was there to say, after all? When the milk was warm enough she poured it into two glasses and placed his within easy reach of his hand.

'It has been a strange day; our wedding day,' she remarked unsteadily with her usual candour. 'Here we are, both dressed for bed, sitting in the kitchen drinking milk in the middle of the night. If someone had to see us now, they would most probably think we're mad.'

'Does it matter what people think?'

'No,' she could not help smiling. 'I was just thinking aloud.'

He reached for her hand and her heart missed a pace as those strong fingers curled about her own. 'Kim,' he said urgently, 'I've also been thinking. When I asked you to marry me, I stipulated that you should think of it as a business arrangement, but . . .' He hesitated with a measure of uncertainty and Kim felt the heavy beat of her heart against her ribs as she waited for him to continue. 'Do you think that . . . given time . . . our marriage might eventually become a true marriage?'

A pulse throbbed painfully in her throat as she stared at his serious features. Did he actually want their marriage to be real? she wondered, hope fluttering and winding its way bravely through her being.

'It might,' she whispered inadequately, not quite certain how to take this new trend in their relationship.

'Do you think you would find it difficult to become my wife in the true sense of the word?'

The uncertain urgency in his voice tore at her heart. 'I don't think I shall find it difficult, Adam,' she told him breathlessly. 'If you'll give me just a little more time?'

His thumb moved caressingly across the back of her hand. 'I shan't force myself on you, Kim, but in time, when we know each other better, we could perhaps discuss this again and come to some satisfactory decision about our future together.'

It was on this promising note that they parted company for the second time that night, and Kim no longer found the thought of the days ahead as something which could only bring eventual heartache. Adam had opened the way to a closer relationship, and although it all sounded rather vague, Kim's happiness depended on it becoming an actuality.

CHAPTER FOUR

THE days slipped by with a swiftness that took Kim's breath away when she stopped to think about it. They had been married a month—a month of long, leisurely days spent walking on the cliff, strolling on the sandy beach, or merely basking in the sun when the weather was warm. For Kim it was a time of becoming acquainted with Adam's various moods—his mockery, his gentleness, his teasing cynicism, and his helpless frustration at his own fumbling inadequacy, which usually culminated in an explosive display of anger directed at anything, and everything close at hand. Usually at Kim, personally.

Winter approached Heron's Bay stealthily, putting a sting into the chilly breeze that blew up from the sea. But this did not somehow prevent Adam and Kim from spending the early part of the evenings in the garden and, as the moon rose over the sea, an audible sigh nearly always escaped Kim.

'You're an incurable romantic, Kim,' Adam accused her one evening with a hint of mockery in his deep voice.

Her glance, swift and angry, was directed at him. 'Is it a crime for a woman to want romance, and to believe in love?'

'No, but what is love?'

'It's the most important reason why people marry. Can you think of any other?' she asked with a touch of sarcasm.

'Yes, I can,' he told her tolerantly. 'What about liking, respect and compatibility? I think they're three of the most important factors in any marriage.'

'But they all stem from love.'

'No, they don't,' he argued, fully aware of her growing agitation, and obviously enjoying it. 'Marriage is the culmination of two different elements thrown together and producing a chemical reaction.'

'Oh, really!'

'For instance,' he continued unperturbed, 'I like you. I like the smell of your hair, the touch of your hands, and the sound of your voice, even when you are ordering me about. I like your laughter, and the way you hum to yourself when you're working in the kitchen.' He turned the full power of his mischievous grin on her. 'You stimulate my thought processes when you argue with me, and you activate my imagination. For this reason you're never boring. In fact, I'm never quite sure what to expect from you, and this I find interesting and intriguing.'

Kim shifted uncomfortably in her seat. 'I wouldn't say that those were good enough reasons for a marriage.'

'That's because you believe in love,' he accused mockingly. 'Love is a much bandied about word which is used for anything and everything on this earth. For example, you could say "I love rock lobster" with just as much intensity as you would say, "I love you" to the woman or man you're holding in your arms, but it doesn't mean that you want to spend the rest of your life with a rock lobster for a bedfellow.'

'Oh, Adam,' she laughed exasperatedly, 'there *is* a difference, you know.'

'Then it's far too subtle for me to discern,' he stated

bluntly, dismissing her statement.

She leaned towards him then, her expression troubled and anxious. 'But it is the only way of expressing exactly what you feel in your heart.'

'There are many other ways of expressing one's feelings, but basically it all has to do with chemistry,' he insisted, and Kim's heart sank. 'Think about it analytically and you'll see that I'm right.'

Kim had no desire to analyse her thoughts at that moment as she clenched her hands and jumped to her feet. 'I'm going inside to start supper,' she announced abruptly. 'Your scientific brain makes me shudder and I shall lose my temper with you if I stay out here a moment longer!'

Adam's mocking laughter followed her inside and she unconsciously lifted her chin in a gesture of defiance. It was impossible to even consider spending the rest of her life with a man who did not believe in love, and mocked its very existence. What sort of life would they have together if his feelings were continually based on scientific conclusions?

Adam came in a few minutes later and found his way quite easily to the kitchen where Kim was preparing supper. She glanced over her shoulder as he entered, but offered him no assistance as he walked up against the table and moved expertly around it to come up behind her. His hands caught at her hair and for a moment he buried his face in it before gripping her shoulders and pulling her back against the lean hardness of his body.

'Are you angry with me?' he asked.

'No.' She trembled at his touch and fought for control over her rising emotions. 'Everyone is entitled to their own opinions, whatever they are.'

'But you don't care very much for mine,' he stated knowingly just above her left ear, his breath fanning her cheek.

'No, I don't,' she acknowledged bluntly, wishing he would not hold her so close.

'They're based on fact and sensible deductions, Kim.'

She turned then and found herself wedged between Adam and the corner cupboard with no way of escape. She glanced up at the man she loved so deeply, and there was an earnest plea for understanding in her eyes which was wasted on him. 'Love isn't something you can sit down and work out on paper like some scientific experiment, Adam,' she explained softly. 'It's something that comes from deep within the human heart, and it's something which can't be cultivated.' She took a deep breath before continuing, 'I could like and admire someone very much. I could find them interesting and exciting, but it still doesn't mean that I could love that person. Nothing on earth would convince me that I should marry someone because we are mentally or scientifically compatible.'

'You married me for far less reason than that.'

Something warned her that they should discontinue this conversation as she saw his eyes become cold flints of steel. 'That's different,' she muttered.

'Would you care to explain?' he persisted.

'Adam, you're twisting me into uncomfortable knots and I don't like it,' she replied, a frightened pulse throbbing at the base of her throat. 'Let's just agree to disagree, and leave it at that. Please, Adam?'

For a moment there was absolute silence, then Adam relaxed visibly. 'You're old-fashioned, Kim, but I like you this way,' he laughed mockingly, sliding his hands down her back towards her hips as he pulled her closer to him. 'It makes you all the more interesting, despite the fact that I shall have to educate you in the scientific workings of the human body.'

'Heaven forbid!' Kim laughed nervously, pushing him away and escaping as quickly as she could from his disturbing nearness.

That night she lay awake, listening to Adam moving about restlessly in his room across the passage. For some time now she had suspected that he was not sleeping well, but, not wishing to intrude unless he approached her for help, she had remained in her own room each night, waiting for his restless pacing to cease before she eventually slept.

She buried her face in her pillow and tried to force herself to sleep, but every fibre of her being was aware of the struggle taking place in the room opposite hers. She could help him, but would he welcome her interference? She hesitated only a moment longer before slipping out of bed and putting on her wrap. Not bothering to put anything on her feet, she padded across the darkened passage to his room. A thin strip of light showed beneath his door, and Kim hesitated with thudding heart before knocking on the door and entering.

He turned towards her, his face haggard. 'Kim?'

'Yes.' She went towards him then, compassion sweeping aside her fear of evoking his anger. 'Are you finding it difficult to sleep?'

'Yes.' His hair stood on end the way his fingers had ploughed through it. 'It's this confounded darkness. The night loses its significance when the day is just as dark. It's sheer hell trying to get through these silent hours each night.'

'I know.'

'How can you know?' he demanded, rounding on her angrily. 'What do *you* know, you who have your sight?'

Kim winced inwardly, but refused to be ruffled. 'If you get into bed, I'll help you to get to sleep.'

'How?' he wanted to know with stinging sarcasm. 'By singing me a lullaby?'

'Stop being so damned sarcastic and self-righteous!' she snapped angrily, shivering slightly at the coldness of the floor beneath her bare feet. 'Let me at least try to help you before you condemn my efforts outright.'

Adam turned away from her and, without a word, removed his dressing gown and climbed into bed. 'Right,' his lips twisted cynically. 'What happens next?'

'This,' said Kim, snapping off the bedside light. 'Now we're both in complete darkness. Well, almost,' she added as the moonlight filtered in through his window.

'Is this part of the therapy?' he asked, and Kim detected a hint of amusement in his voice that made her blush in the darkness.

Without replying she sat down beside him on the small single bed and took his hand in hers. 'I often used to sit like this with my father,' she confided in him, her voice low and reassuring. 'Sometimes we talked about silly little things that really meant nothing, and quite often I just sat with him in silence until he slept.'

'I think I'm beginning to understand,' Adam said after a while, almost as if he had made an astonishing discovery.

'Are you?' Kim asked warily, looking down at the

dark outline of his head on the pillow. 'My father always maintained that the silence at night became a threat to him. He said it ruled his mind and twisted his thoughts until he was certain he would go mad. It was, of course, that feeling of being completely isolated from the rest of the world, and that was when the touch of a hand or the sound of a voice was so important to him.' She moved her hand slightly and felt the responding pressure of his fingers. 'You see, Adam, I do understand. You need just that little bit of assurance that you're not alone.'

'What would I have done without you, Kim?' he sighed heavily, and she knew instinctively that he had relaxed completely.

'Don't say that,' she reprimanded gently. 'No one is ever entirely alone. There's always Someone there when we're in need.'

There was a brief silence before his whispered query reached her ears. 'Do you mean God?'

'Yes . . . and don't overwhelm me with scientific theories to prove that God doesn't exist,' she added quickly before he could interrupt.

'I may not believe in love, Kim,' he rebuked her, 'but I do believe in God.'

'And God is love,' she could not help quoting, and this Adam could not dispute.

According to the luminous hands of the clock, she sat with him for almost an hour, long after his regular breathing had indicated that he was asleep. She held his hand, reluctant to leave him, until her aching limbs forced her to slip her hand from his and rise to her feet, biting back a cry of pain as the blood shot into her numbed legs.

Kim held her breath as he murmured her name, but he merely turned over on to his side and slept on. She hovered a moment longer beside his bed with a feeling of indescribable tenderness as she looked down at his sleeping form, then, smothering a yawn behind her hand, she tiptoed from his room and sought the comfort of her own bed.

Adam was less sceptical after that night, welcoming her soothing presence with obvious relief on other occasions when sleep evaded him, and it forged a bond between them that grew stronger as time passed.

The peaceful tranquillity of their life had to end some time, Kim knew, and, although she dreaded the thought, she realised that they could not continue shutting their minds to the future. Adam would have to return to the life he knew before his accident had made him seek the solitude of Heron's Bay, and she would have to guide him in that direction, even if it meant that she would no longer be needed.

'Let's go out in the motorboat,' Adam suggested one morning when the air was still and warm. His restless energy disturbed her, but she refrained from commenting on his unusual behaviour.

'You can steer this thing, can't you?' Adam asked matter-of-factly when they eventually clambered aboard his boat.

'Of course I can,' she replied indignantly as she sat down behind the wheel. 'I had a boy-friend once who owned a boat.'

'Oh?' His smile was gently mocking. 'What happened to the boy-friend?'

Kim turned the key in the ignition and the engine

sprang to life. 'He was here on holiday, and I was in my last year at school,' she shouted above the noise. 'For the first time in my life I was smitten, but it was a romantic crush that lasted only for the length of his holiday.'

'Did you sometimes wish that you could have resumed your relationship with him?'

'No, never!' she shouted emphatically. 'He had pimples.'

Adam's unexpected roar of laughter was drowned by the revving of the engine as she steered out to sea.

This suggested pleasure-trip turned out to be disastrous for Adam. The choppy, swaying movement of his sleek vessel had an adverse effect on him, and his enjoyment soon diminished. One glance at his pale, taut features told her that he was fighting against a rising nausea.

'Go back!' he shouted urgently even as she turned the boat about and headed back to the shore, where the small jetty jutted out into the sea.

Kim eased the boat into the private enclosure and cut the engine before tying it securely to its moorings. She turned to Adam then and almost cried out at the look of utter dejection on his pale face.

'Adam, are you all right?'

'Yes,' he replied, grinding his teeth. 'Don't panic, just get me out of here.'

Moments later, with the steadiness of the jetty beneath his feet, he clutched at Kim as if for support. 'I'm sorry, Kim,' he groaned, the colour returning to his cheeks as he held her closer to him.

'Don't apologise, Adam,' she whispered reassuringly against his chest, her arms sliding about his waist in a comforting gesture as she felt him tremble. 'I understand, and I should have known better.'

'It was the motion of the boat beneath me, and not being able to see——'

'I know,' she interrupted swiftly. 'You don't have to explain.'

Adam's hand moved against her cheek and found its way into her hair, and then, for the first time since their wedding day, his hard mouth found hers with remarkable accuracy. Surprise made her stiffen against him, her lips unresponsive beneath his despite the wild beating of her heart. 'Don't read too much into this kiss,' she warned herself as she fought down her clamouring emotions.

'Shall we go home now?' she asked unsteadily when he finally raised his head, and he nodded briefly, keeping his arm about her as they walked along the beach towards the steps leading up the cliff.

That afternoon a letter arrived for Adam with a Cape Town postmark. 'Shall I read it to you?' Kim asked unthinkingly.

'How shall I know what's in it if you don't read it to me?' he snapped irritably, and Kim bit her lip nervously.

She tore open the envelope and extracted the letter. It was a single page written in a masculine handwriting, she noticed as she glanced down at the signature. 'It's from someone who signs himself Bill Stewart.'

Adam nodded briefly, sucking at his pipe. 'He's a scientist at the Scientific Institute.'

Without waiting for further information, Kim read the letter to Adam. It started with the usual enquiries as to his health and then swung directly to the reason for communicating. 'The directors have been understandably reluctant to replace you as Chief of the Scientific Institute,' Kim read aloud, discovering for the first time the important position he had held, 'and have asked me to negotiate with you in this matter. They have put forward a few suggestions which might interest you, and hasten your return. Let me know when it would be convenient for you to see me, then I shall take a day off and drive out to Heron's Bay to discuss the details with you.

'There is an element of extreme urgency, as you well know, and it's more than my job is worth to mention it on paper. Regards, Bill Stewart.'

Adam clenched his teeth about the stem of his pipe and frowned heavily, offering no comment.

'Will you see him, Adam?' Kim asked eventually when she could bear the silence no longer.

'No! Of what use am I to the Institute as I am?'

She cast him a startled glance. 'How can you say that when you don't even know what they have in mind?'

'I don't want their pity.'

'Who said anything about pity?' she demanded angrily. 'Really, Adam, you're being rather obstinate. At least see this man and let him explain before you flatly refuse what they may have to offer. You can't spend the rest of your life hibernating from the rest of the world, fighting off reality.'

'You seem to forget,' he said in a tight-lipped fashion, 'I'm blind.'

'What difference does that make?' Kim pressed on regardless of the consequences. 'You may be blind, Adam, but there's nothing wrong with your brain, so why not use it instead of letting all that information go to waste?'

He got to his feet, clearly agitated by her persistence, for he kicked a small table out of his way and sent it skidding across the floor. 'For the last time, Kim,' he said harshly, 'I will *not* see Bill, and I will *not* accept their charity.'

Kim shivered at the finality in his voice. 'It appears as though there's some urgency,' she continued bravely, jumping nervously as he swung round to face her, his sightless eyes pinning her ruthlessly to her chair.

'The matter is urgent,' he ground out the words, 'but there are others who can continue where I left off.'

'Are you sure?' Adam remained silent and she regained her confidence. 'Would you mind if I saw Mr Stewart and found out exactly what they have in mind?'

'It won't help,' he argued stubbornly.

'If I were you, I would at least like to know what it is I'm refusing.'

Her words hung heavily in the air between them, but Adam had obviously digested the suggestion, for a smile of resignation hovered about his lips. 'If it will make you feel better, then write to him and make an appointment to see him. But I must warn you that your efforts will be futile.'

That same evening after dinner, Kim wrote to Bill Stewart and, after introducing herself as Adam's wife, suggested that they meet each other at the only existing cafe in Heron's Bay on a date that would suit him. She did not omit mentioning Adam's reluctance to return to the Institute, but suggested that if she knew more about the proposition, she might be able to persuade him otherwise.

73

With the letter addressed, sealed and ready to be posted, Kim went to bed that night with a feeling that hovered between anticipation and fear. What would the future hold for Adam and herself? she wondered as she tossed about in bed. If there was a chance that he could resume a semblance of his former life, then she could not restrain him, but what would a change like that hold for her personally?

Her thoughts kept her awake for some time before she noticed that Adam, too, was having difficulty in getting to sleep. Was he thinking about his future just as she was? Would he let his blindness stand in his way permanently? She shrugged off her thoughts and reached for her wrap at the foot of her bed.

'Can't you sleep?' she asked moments later as she entered his room to find him pacing the floor.

'No.'

'Neither can I,' she admitted truthfully, helping him back into bed and snapping off the light.

Adam's hand reached for hers as she sat down beside him on the bed, and for some time they remained like that, holding hands in silence, until he suddenly removed his hand from hers and found her shoulder. The pressure of his fingers sent tremors along her nerves and, holding her breath, she wondered at this sudden digression from their normal routine.

'Kim,' he said softly, his hand now finding her cheek and gently caressing her neck, 'I'm sorry that the day turned out so disastrous.'

'I told you not to apologise,' she reprimanded, keeping a tight control on her tremulous voice.

His hand went round to the nape of her neck and she was pulled unresistingly towards him until his mouth

74

found hers. Unlike that morning, her lips were instantly responsive against the demanding pressure of his. He held her with both arms now, his hands caressing her and arousing emotions she had thought herself incapable of experiencing. Trembling and unable to resist, she clung to him as his hand slid beneath her wrap, moving urgently against her shoulder before exploring lower.

'Kim?' he groaned against her lips, and her name was a plea for acceptance which her loving heart could not deny, for the urgency of her own need was as great as his.

'Yes, Adam. Yes,' she whispered as he pulled her down beside him, and then, unable to think of anything other than the demanding pressure of his lips and arms, she allowed herself to be swept along on a seemingly never-ending tide of rapture.

Kim awoke the following morning with the unfamiliar weight of Adam's arm flung across her waist. As memories of the previous evening came flooding back, she felt no shame as she recalled the awe-inspiring emotions awakened within her by the gentleness of his caressing touch. There had been no fear; no withdrawal at the last moment, only a complete surrendering of herself as his whispered endearments added to the rapture in the fusion of mind and body.

She turned her head and glanced at his face only inches from hers on the pillow, and felt an overwhelming rush of tenderness warm her heart, accelerating its steady pace. His taut features were relaxed in sleep, making him appear almost boyish, with his hair tousled and lying across his forehead. She loved him with a burning intensity she had not thought possible, and she would continue to love him even if he should eventually have no further need of her and sent her away, she thought agonisingly as she slid carefully from beneath his restraining arm without waking him.

Bathed and dressed, she went down to the kitchen to make some coffee, and for some time she stood and watched the sun rising in the east like a glowing ball of fire. 'How different everything looks this morning. How fresh and new,' she thought, bemused. She felt different as well. She had become a woman overnight; a woman who had been made aware of her own needs and desires, and of emotional heights she had not known existed until Adam took it upon himself to educate her.

A step behind her made her turn and the object of her thoughts stood before her in dressing gown and slippers, and still unshaven. She met his glance and blushed furiously despite the fact that she knew he could not see her. 'I thought you were still asleep,' she said.

He smiled briefly. 'I heard you moving about in the kitchen and decided to come down and have my coffee with you.'

'You're just in time, I'm about to pour.'

'Kim,' he said urgently, reaching for her and pulling her unresistingly towards him, 'about last night . . . have you any regrets?'

'None at all,' she assured him, aware of the heavy beat of his heart beneath her fingertips. 'Have you?'

There was a hint of remorse on his face. 'Only that I actually had no right——'

'You had every right, Adam,' she interrupted him adamantly, clutching at his shoulders and shaking him slightly. 'I'm your wife.'

'Yes,' he acknowledged with a trace of the old mockery as he bent his dark head and rubbed his rough cheek against hers. 'You are my wife, and no one can dispute that fact now, unless you want our marriage to go back to what it was?'

'No!' She buried her flushed face against him, standing on tiptoe to slide her arms about his neck. 'No, I don't. I . . . want to be your wife, Adam.'

'In every sense of the word?'

The rough warmth of his lips against her neck was creating havoc with her emotions. 'In every possible way, but only if you wish it too.'

'I do wish it, my dearest Kim,' he murmured against her lips. 'Amid all the uncertainties of this world, that is one thing you can be absolutely sure of. I do want you.'

The demanding pressure of his lips confirmed his statement and inflamed her with a pulsating desire that changed her from the level-headed person she was to a trembling bundle of acquiescence. If only he would tell her that he loved her! If only he would say it . . . just once, her heart cried, but she knew somehow that those were words she would never hear from Adam. Wanting her as his wife had not altered his way of reasoning, and she would have to be satisfied with his scientific approach regarding their marriage.

'I think I should pour that coffee,' she remarked tremulously, an unusual brightness in her green eyes which only he could put there as she breathlessly warded off any further advances.

'I believe you're shy,' Adam teased her gently. 'You weren't shy last night, or does the cold light of day make a difference to the way you feel?'

'I don't feel any different,' she protested, her cheeks stinging with embarrassment. 'It's just that I——'

'Find it difficult to face me this morning?' he finished for her humorously. 'You're well protected, Kim. I can't see you . . . only touch you,' he added in a way that made her skin tingle as if he had actually done just that.

'Adam,' she whispered anxiously, 'don't tease me.'

His face sobered instantly as he caught hold of her hand and carried it to his lips. 'I shan't tease you, my dear Kim. Your shyness is part of the enchantment you represent for me, and it's something I shall cherish.'

CHAPTER FIVE

Life for Kim had assumed a totally different pattern and had gained a new significance. Adam moved into her room, with the more comfortable double bed, as if it was the most natural thing on earth, and her blushes came and went unnoticed. As the colder weather set in, they spent long, unforgettable evenings at the fireside, satisfied just to sit and talk in whispers until Kim's head became heavy with sleep on his shoulder.

Bill Stewart telephoned one evening to say that he would be driving through to Heron's Bay the following day, and because of this Adam was instantly on the defensive.

'I shan't see him,' he insisted stubbornly, scowling at nothing in particular.

'You won't have to see him . . . initially,' she said

haltingly, 'but if I think that his suggestions are reasonable, I shall bring him up here to the cottage and you'll see him and speak to him yourself.'

'Kim, you're wasting your time.'

'We'll see!' she muttered, smiling to herself. She could be just as determined as Adam, but she was so sure that it was merely pride that was keeping him from doing the work he loved that she was almost willing to bet on it.

Bill Stewart was not at all what Kim had expected. He was a short, stockily built man with a shock of red hair and hazel eyes that appeared to be continually dancing with merriment, even when he was at his most serious.

'I must say it was a surprise to discover that old Adam had finally taken the plunge into matrimony,' he remarked as they faced each other across a small table in the only tea room Heron's Bay had to offer. 'We all thought that when he did, his choice would fall on . . . well, perhaps this isn't the time to discuss this subject.'

Kim regarded him steadily in the gloomy atmosphere of the café and noticed his cheeks colouring faintly with embarrassment. 'You've intrigued me, Mr Stewart. Won't you continue with what you were saying?'

He swallowed a mouthful of tea and moved his shoulders uncomfortably. 'Adam used to knock about quite a bit with Ursula Bennett, a fellow scientist. At the time we thought that he was serious about her, but we were obviously mistaken. Adam has never been predictable in his actions.'

Just how serious had Adam been about this Ursula Bennett? Kim wondered curiously. If it had not been for the accident, would he have married her? But these

79

were painful thoughts which were best left in the past, she decided as she concentrated on her companion.

'Shall we get down to the purpose of your visit?' she said.

'Certainly,' his eyes twinkled and an involuntary smile plucked at her lips. 'We need Adam desperately to complete the job he was working on before the accident. Like so many clever men, he seldom made a note of anything, and preferred keeping his information to himself. We want him back as our Chief Scientist, and we're prepared to be as accommodating as he wishes.'

Kim's hackles rose sharply. 'Mr Stewart——'

'Bill,' he interrupted swiftly. 'Call me Bill, Kim. Adam and I are old friends.'

'Very well . . . Bill,' her anger simmered as she frowned at him. 'I must warn you never to use the word accommodating when speaking to Adam. To speak of accommodating his wishes smacks of pity, and that's something he abhors.'

'I've never known Adam to be touchy,' he said.

'Blindness often affects one in that way,' Kim said quietly, and convincingly. 'Tell me,' she questioned as the silence lengthened uncomfortably between them, 'In which way do you plan to assist him?'

'Well . . .' he glanced at her quickly and Kim detected a slight nervousness. 'He's always worked very closely with Ursula Bennett in the past. She knows his methods better than anyone else, so it was decided to make her his personal assistant.'

Kim crushed the quiver of apprehension that raced through her. So Ursula Bennett was to be brought back into his life prominently, she thought anxiously. And just how would this arrangement affect her own life? Would Adam, once he had found his feet, want to continue his previous relationship with his former girl-friend? Would he regret his hasty decision to marry someone else?

'In other words,' she swallowed with difficulty, 'Ursula Bennett could give him the visual assistance he would require.'

'Exactly.'

'I must not stand in his way,' Kim warned herself as she stared through the window in thoughtful silence at the street beyond. She could see nothing except the rigid disapproval on Adam's face when she left the cottage that morning to meet Bill Stewart. If only he would realise that she was doing this for his own good, instead of which he considered that she was deliberately torturing him. She sighed heavily and returned her attention to her companion, to find his speculative glance resting on her.

'Tell me about the accident,' she asked him, steering the conversation away from the main topic for a while. 'How did it happen?'

Bill offered her a cigarette, but when she refused he lit one for himself and blew the smoke forcefully into the air. 'Owing to the negligence of one of the laboratory assistants there was an explosion which killed one man, and blinded Adam.'

'But his eyes aren't damaged. I mean——'

'Can you imagine what an explosion in a laboratory is like?' he questioned seriously. 'Chemicals were exploding and there was glass flying about all over the place. Adam was the only person nearest the source of the explosion, other than the chap who was killed, and when I visited him in hospital after the accident I remember him expressing the wish that he had died as well. I laughed at him then, but I had no idea how serious his injuries were.'

'It is serious, then?'

'Very.' He frowned at the tip of his cigarette. 'A shiver of glass penetrated the corner of his eye and damaged the optic nerve.'

'Can't they operate?'

'Apparently not. As far as I could understand at the time, no one was prepared to risk it.' His glance was curious. 'Why are you asking me all these questions? Hasn't he told you?'

Kim lowered her lashes and coloured slightly. 'Adam has never wanted to be questioned on the subject.'

'If I know Adam he most probably blames himself for the accident,' Bill told her with a touch of bitterness. 'He always was a great one for carrying the responsibilities of others on his shoulders.'

'Adam must return to his work,' Kim remarked with some urgency. 'He can't sit around idly all day, it's wearing him out, but he's as stubborn as a mule. He needs to regain a certain amount of normality in his life in order to gain confidence in himself once more.'

'Do you think you'll be able to persuade him to see me?' Bill asked, glancing at her from beneath his bushy eyebrows as he crushed his cigarette into the ashtray.

Could she persuade Adam to see Bill, or would his trip down to Heron's Bay have been futile? Bill had remarked that Adam was not predictable, and Kim was forced to acknowledge this. There was no way of knowing just how Adam would react to Bill's suggestions.

'I'm going to stick my neck out and say yes,' she replied, feeling less confident than she sounded. 'Will you give me a lift up to the cottage and give me the opportunity to speak to Adam first?'

Bill pushed back his chair and stood up with his briefcase in his hand. 'Kim, I'll do anything you say . . . if it will help encourage Adam to return.'

Neither of them said a word until Bill had parked the car on the grass verge in front of the cottage. 'If you hear a bout of shouting going on,' she warned lightly as she turned to face him, 'pay no heed. Once the shouting is over he usually ends up being sensible.'

Bill grinned at her. 'Good luck!'

Adam was pacing the floor of the lounge when she entered the cottage. 'I've seen Bill Stewart,' she said with forced casualness, shedding her coat and seating herself in the nearest chair. 'Are you listening, Adam?'

'Yes, I'm listening,' he said harshly, turning his back on her. 'Am I correct in assuming that he's waiting outside in his car for the all clear from you?'

'Yes.' Her heart was thumping against her ribs.

Adam paced about the room with more vigour. 'Well, you can tell him right now that he can go back to where he came from. He's wasting his time.'

Kim strove for a calmness she was far from experiencing. 'Adam, sit down. I can't talk to you when you persist in marching up and down. It makes my head spin, and it makes me nervous.'

'Stop ordering me about!'

'You're shouting,' she reprimanded, raising her voice a fraction.

'I will damn well shout if I want to!'

Kim rose swiftly to her feet and caught at the sleeve

83

of his jacket, turning him forcibly to face her. 'Adam, will you believe that I want only what's best for you?'

His lips tightened harshly. 'I very much doubt that.'

She winced. 'You're being unkind!'

'Kim, I refuse to be pitied. I won't have it!' he stated furiously, and she could almost feel the anger vibrating through his body beneath her hands. 'If I return to the Institute I can just imagine the pitying stares of my colleagues. They would make concessions for me which they would never dream of doing for others; they would carefully avoid using words like 'look' and 'see' to the point of madness for fear of drawing attention to my blindness; and when I enter a room they'll jump to my assistance while they sympathetically guide me around the various objects.' He gestured bitterly. 'Oh, I could go on and on. I don't want to be treated like a freak.'

'Pity and compassion are two human emotions one need never be ashamed of,' she told him bluntly. 'It's only natural that they would feel that way.'

'Well, I don't want any part of it, thank you!'

'Adam, be honest with me,' she pleaded, trying to reason with him calmly. 'If the position was reversed, would you not feel the same as they would?'

He hesitated a moment, but the tenseness did not leave him. 'Naturally, but that doesn't alter the fact——'

'Adam, sit down and listen to me,' she interrupted, pushing him down on to the couch. 'Trust me, please.' She took another deep breath and continued, 'During these weeks we've spent together something has happened to you without your even realising it. With or without your dark glasses, you have the uncanny knack of looking directly at me. If you stretched out your hand at this moment, you would know exactly where I am to touch me. You've learnt to walk about this cottage completely unaided, and without bumping into the furniture.' She stopped for a moment to make sure that she held his attention. 'These are the things that are worrying you most, they're keeping you from what you want most to do, and it need not be so. You're afraid that you might make a fool of yourself, but you are unnecessarily afraid. Naturally, there are going to be a few minor spills at first, but only until you find your way around.'

Adam was silent for a moment before he pulled her down beside him. 'I wish I had your confidence, my understanding Kim.'

She rested her head on his shoulder for a moment and brushed her lips lightly against his cheek. 'Think of it as a challenge which could lead to complete independence. You must admit, Adam, that it's worth a try.'

'And when and if I gain complete independence, will that be your cue to leave me?' There was a touch of urgency in his voice that did not escape her. 'Are you hoping to gain your freedom?'

'I shall stay with you for as long as you want me, Adam,' she promised with a warmth and sincerity he could not fail to hear.

His kiss was long and lingering with an undercurrent of passion that never failed to arouse her. He raised his head suddenly and said tersely, 'Perhaps you'd better tell me what Bill had to say before we go any further.'

Kim explained swiftly, but could not discern anything from Adam's expression, for it remained inscrutable. 'There are, of course, other factors which only Bill could explain to you,' she concluded hopefully, 'but it all sounds quite reasonable to me.'

A long silence followed that set her nerves on edge. Through the lounge window she could see Bill Stewart leaning against the bonnet of his car, smoking a cigarette. Was he, too, beginning to feel the strain of waiting? she wondered sympathetically.

'Tell Bill to come in,' Adam said with a suddenness that made her jump with fright. 'You suggested once that I should know exactly what it was that I'm refusing, so let him in and let's get it over with.'

The first hurdle had been overcome, Kim thought triumphantly as she went about the kitchen preparing the evening dinner. It was now up to Bill Stewart to convince Adam that he should take the next step, and Bill was certainly taking his time about it so as not to give Adam the impression that he was being pushed into something he was not ready for.

Kim had thought it best to leave them alone in the lounge, and they had remained closeted there until she was forced to call them for lunch. With Adam's approval she had persuaded Bill to stay the night, and now, with no sign of them emerging from the lounge, she went upstairs to prepare Adam's old room for Bill. What would have happened, she wondered humorously, if Bill had arrived during the first few weeks after their marriage? He would certainly have found it strange that, with two bedrooms in the cottage, there was no place for him to sleep other than on the couch in the lounge.

It was late that afternoon when she heard Bill calling to her where she was busy turning the roast in the oven. 'Adam wants to know if you're experiencing a drought in the kitchen.'

'I suppose he wants coffee,' she laughed, emerging from the kitchen looking totally different in a warm woollen dress with an apron tied about her waist, and she was well aware of Bill's appreciative glance as she handed him the tray of coffee. 'I had a feeling that it wouldn't be long before Adam started shouting for liquid refreshment,' she explained mischievously as she disposed of her apron and followed him to the lounge where Adam sat waiting with a self-satisfied grin on his face.

'I timed it well, didn't I?' he remarked with casual laziness, taking the hand she had placed on his shoulder and pressing his warm lips against her palm.

She lowered her head and brushed her lips against his lean cheek. 'Has it ever occurred to you that it's perhaps I who know you so well, my dear Adam?'

Bill stood there holding the tray, his eyebrows raised comically. 'When the two of you have done with complimenting yourselves, may we get down to the business of having our coffee?'

'Sorry, Bill,' Kim laughed apologetically. 'Put the tray on the table and help yourself. I'll get Adam's and my own.'

'Adam was telling me how the two of you met,' Bill said eventually when there was a lull in the conversation. 'That was fate if ever there was.'

Kim nodded and glanced at Adam, but he appeared to have sunk into a world consisting of his own thoughts. 'Well?' she prompted nervously. 'What have you decided?'

Adam surfaced reluctantly, his lips firmly compressed. 'I haven't decided anything yet. I would like to sleep on it first.'

She snorted in disbelief. 'If I know you, you won't sleep at all.'

'Perhaps not,' he agreed thoughtfully, 'but it's not something I want to take on without careful consideration. There's too much at stake . . . for everyone concerned.'

Kim's glance met Bill's and in his eyes she saw the look of a man who, after laying all his cards on the table, found that he had no ace up his sleeve with which to swing the favour in his direction. All he could do was to wait, she realised as some of his tension and apprehensiveness rubbed off on to her.

After dinner that evening, Adam seemed to snap out of his gloom and they spent a pleasurable evening in front of the fire in the lounge. Adam amazed Kim even further by discussing incidents which had occurred before his accident, something which he had not done before. She listened thankfully as Bill talked to him quite naturally, as though nothing had happened to mar Adam's memories. Bill must have guessed her feelings for he sent her a reassuring smile that released some of the tension which had been building up inside of her during the day.

Kim was burning with curiosity to know more about Ursula Bennett, but she did not have the nerve to swing the conversation in that direction. How did Adam feel about the prospect of working so closely with this woman? Did it please him? Would he look forward to it?

She shook herself free of these disturbing thoughts

and tried to concentrate on the conversation between Adam and Bill, but they were becoming so technically involved that she went through to the kitchen instead to make them something to drink.

It was late when they eventually went to bed that night, but in spite of this Kim found that she could not sleep. Her mind was much too occupied with uncomfortable thoughts of the future. She wanted Adam to return to his work, yet there was something about this whole venture that she feared. What was it? Ursula Bennett? No, not entirely. It was something she could not define, but it was there all the same, and no amount of reasoning could dispense with it.

Adam, too, seemed to be unusually restless until he eventually pushed himself up on his elbow and leaned closer to her. 'Are you awake, Kim?'

'Yes, Adam.'

'I must talk to you,' he said, pulling her into his arms, and his nearness at that moment was balm to her disturbing thoughts. 'How good are you at keeping things to yourself?'

'That depends on what it is that has to be kept secret,' she replied in a subdued voice and with a certain amount of amusement.

'It involves state security.'

Kim's heart leapt beneath his hand. 'Then, of course, nothing would induce me to speak of it.'

There was a moment of tense silence before he continued, almost as if he were weighing the justification of his desire to confide in her. 'Before the accident, Kim, I was working tentatively on plans for a new military weapon,' he confessed in a hushed voice. 'It appears now that the government is very interested in the completion of such a weapon, and it's somewhat urgent.'

'If you're aware of the urgency, why are you so hesitant about returning?' she wanted to know.

'It's going to mean hours of work, Kim—all day at the Institute and quite possibly the evenings at home.' His fingers worked their way through her hair, tugging gently at the silken strands. 'It means that we shall have very little time together.'

'It's something I shall have to learn to accept,' she whispered into his neck. Then a new thought arose in her mind. 'Will the evenings you have to work at home involve Ursula Bennett?'

'I have no doubt that it will involve her,' he replied cautiously. 'Why?'

'Just curious.'

'No, my Kim, there's more than curiosity there. I think Bill has told you a little something about Ursula.' His arms tightened about her slender figure and quite suddenly he was bending over her, his face inches from hers in the moonlit darkness. 'Am I right?'

'Yes,' she admitted truthfully, ashamed at the spark of jealousy which had been aroused within her.

'You have nothing to fear, you know.'

'I wonder,' Kim thought anxiously as his lips found hers. Would he still feel the same once he was in daily contact with this woman whom she knew only by name? Adam's lips finally came to rest on the tempting hollow in her throat, and she trembled against him.

'So you're going back after all, despite your initial stubbornness,' she remarked, trying to ignore the sensations caused by the exploratory touch of his lips.

Adam released her unexpectedly and fell back against his pillows. 'I haven't decided yet.'

'Oh, yes, you have, Adam Granger,' she accused lightly. 'Why don't you admit that you're longing to get back to work? That you're thrilled to bits at the thought?'

'All right, I am,' he acknowledged abruptly, 'but it doesn't erase all those other factors I mentioned. I don't want anyone's pity.'

Kim sat up in bed. 'Have you ever thought of the possibility that your colleagues might be well aware of this fact?'

'Kim, stop it!' He pulled her down against him with a fierceness that made her breasts hurt against the hardness of his chest. 'Between Bill and yourself I'm becoming convinced that I've behaved like a touchy fool.'

'You have every right to be touchy, Adam, but you're not a fool,' she managed, warding off his lips.

'Thank you, my dear, you've always done a good job of boosting my morale,' he sighed, and this time she gave him her lips and welcomed the touch of his warm hands against her skin.

'You are going back, aren't you?' she demanded before his kisses became too urgent. 'Adam, are you?'

'You're like a dog that won't let go of a bone,' he muttered in exasperation. 'Stop nagging, Kim!'

'But you are, aren't you?' she persisted, determined to know his decision before she could settle down to sleep.

'Yes, I think so.'

Kim felt curiously triumphant, but her thoughts were instantly practical. 'Where shall we stay?'

'Didn't I tell you that I have a flat in Cape Town?' he asked with some amazement.

'No, you didn't.'

'It's a penthouse, actually, but you'll like it.'

For some time they lay in silence listening to the sound of the sea and the crickets chirping in the undergrowth, until another sound made them listen more intently. It was the definite sound of someone's footsteps pacing softly back and forth.

'Why don't you go and put poor Bill out of his misery?' she suggested at last, extricating herself from Adam's arms. 'Tell him that you've decided to accept what they have to offer you so that the poor man can get some sleep instead of spending the night pacing the floor.'

Adam muttered something about getting no peace, but he nevertheless put on his dressing gown and went to the door. 'Bill!' he called loudly across the landing, and the door opposite opened almost instantly.

'Yes?'

'Kim said I should tell you to stop worrying,' Adam told their surprised guest. 'I'll go back to work.'

Delighted, Bill slapped his hand against his thigh. 'Hell, I think I need a drink.'

'What about a strong cup of coffee for all of us?' Kim suggested, tightening the belt of her dressing gown as she came up behind Adam.

'Splendid idea,' both men agreed almost simultaneously.

'I'll go and put the kettle on,' Kim murmured, unable to hide her smile of amusement as she brushed past Adam.

Once again the cottage was ablaze with lights as they

trooped down to the kitchen. This was quite probably the most enjoyable part of the whole day as they sat round the kitchen table sipping strong coffee and conversing without the tension which had been so evident earlier in the evening.

'How soon do you think you could be in Cape Town?' Bill asked eventually, his hazel eyes dancing with merriment at having succeeded in his mission.

Adam frowned slightly. 'Well, today is Thursday.'

Kim's glance went swiftly to the clock on the wall. 'Correction, today is Friday.'

Bill slapped his forehead. 'Good heavens, is it that late?'

'It was after eleven when we came down to the kitchen,' Kim reminded him with a grin.

'What if Kim and I drive up on Saturday morning?' Adam intervened, the frown reappearing on his forehead. 'That will give us the week-end to settle in, and I could start work on Monday.'

'That sounds fine to me,' Bill agreed readily. 'I'll drop in on you on Sunday afternoon to make sure you've settled in comfortably, and to find out if there's anything you may need. We could also make the final arrangements.'

'Well, that's settled, then,' Kim sighed, placing the cups in the basin and rinsing them quickly. 'I don't know what the two of you are going to do, but I'm going to bed.'

She went up ahead of them, pausing for a moment on the landing to watch their steady progress up the stairs. To see Adam like this made it difficult to believe that he was blind, she could not help marvelling once more. He took the steps accurately even while in conversation with Bill, his hand sliding along the balustrade without gripping. Soon, she thought, soon he would be entirely independent, and when this was so, would there be a place for her in his life after all? Would the time they spent together here at Heron's Bay have meant as much to him as it did to her?

CHAPTER SIX

KIM went down to the village, soon after Bill Stewart left the following morning, to make arrangements for Adam's motorboat to be taken care of, and also to pay a brief visit to the manse. Mr Wilson and his wife would never have forgiven her if they had left without saying goodbye.

'So Adam has finally been persuaded to return to the Institute,' Mr Wilson remarked as he joined his wife and Kim for tea in the living-room. 'I didn't think he would be able to remain idle for very long.'

'I'm very happy for Adam's sake that he has decided to pick up the threads of his life,' Kim told her friends, careful not to mention her own doubts and fears for the future.

'I hope you won't be selling the cottage?' Mrs Wilson said with swift concern. 'You've been so happy there.'

'Oh, no, we shan't be selling, at least . . .' Kim bit her lip. 'Adam hasn't said anything about selling.'

She felt quite disturbed about this, but she was determined that, if it were at all possible, she would not allow Adam to sell the cottage.

Adam waited rather impatiently for Kim's return.

Now that he had decided to return to the city, he was anxious to get it over with, he told her as she helped him pack a few of the books he wanted to take with him.

Their last night at Heron's Bay was filled with nostalgia for Kim, and she wondered sadly whether they would ever be able to recapture the times they had spent there together. Life in the city was going to be vastly different from what she had become accustomed to, and Adam, she knew, would somehow change as well. It was something she would have to expect and accept, no matter how difficult.

Ursula Bennett! What was she like? Kim wondered curiously as she lay listening to Adam's regular breathing beside her. She had been tempted to question him more closely, but felt somehow that he would not appreciate being questioned about the woman who had meant so much to him in the past. Would Ursula resent the fact that someone else had taken her place in Adam's life? Kim considered this question for some time, but it was difficult to decide when she had no idea what Ursula was actually like. She would just have to wait and see, she decided eventually as she fell asleep.

'Can you drive?' Adam asked dubiously the following morning as they were about to leave for the city.

Kim glanced at him with some amusement. 'Of course.'

'Don't tell me,' he mocked, putting on his dark glasses. 'You had a boy-friend with a car.'

'No,' she denied laughingly. 'My aunt taught me to drive in her old car, but I sold it soon after her death. It had become a rattling death-trap anyway.'

The Peugeot stood packed and ready, but still Adam hesitated. 'Have you a driver's licence?'

'Yes,' she said abruptly, with a touch of sarcasm. 'Would you like to see it?'

The silence hung heavily between them and Kim felt slightly sick. It was the first time she had passed such a thoughtless remark, and it stung her more deeply than she would have him guess.

Except for the barely perceptible tightening of his lips, Adam gave no indication that her foolish remark had upset him. She could almost believe that he had not heard . . . but there was no doubt that he had.

'As with everything else, I'll have to take your word for it,' he said finally, and Kim thought it best not to offer her apologies at that moment.

She locked the front door behind them and at the gate she turned for the last time to gaze at the cottage with a rising lump in her throat. Her happiness here had been brief, but wonderful. Something she would remember.

'If you don't come now, we'll never get away,' Adam remarked irritably from the car.

'Just coming,' she sighed, throwing her hair back over her shoulder as she caught sight of a seagull swooping low over the cottage, dipping its wings as if in salute.

If Adam had suffered any nervousness at the onset of their journey, it soon evaporated as the kilometres sped by. He lowered his seat, relaxed, and finally slept. It was a lonely journey for Kim, but she preferred having Adam's sleeping form beside her than to have him nervous and jumpy at every movement she made.

While her aunt was still alive and well enough to travel, they had often travelled from Heron's Bay to

Cape Town, and usually remained in the city a day or two. But on those occasions the journey had never been pleasant, for there was always the nagging fear that Aunt Freda's car might leave them in the lurch on a lonely stretch of road. On this occasion, however, it was quite the reverse, for Adam's car was in perfect order, and Kim could allow herself the pleasure of enjoying the lush scenery as it floated past.

When Table Mountain came into view, she reduced speed to admire its majestic beauty for a moment as it towered above the city. It was a pleasing sight that never failed to thrill her each time she saw it, and she felt strangely excited at the prospect of living virtually in its shadows.

As she approached the outskirts of the city, she turned off the road and shook Adam lightly. 'We're almost there, and you'll have to direct me.'

'Tell me when you've reached the Heerengracht,' he replied, instantly awake as he sat up and readjusted his seat. 'I'll direct you from there.'

This was the most nerve-racking part of the journey, having Adam direct her through part of the city towards Sea Point on a Saturday morning when the traffic was at its peak. Fortunately for her, she made no errors, and they reached the building which housed Adam's penthouse without any mishap. She parked the car in the garage he had indicated and started off-loading. It took only one trip up in the lift, but when they reached the door to Adam's penthouse, she experienced a nervous quivering at the pit of her stomach. It was done. It was over. The move had been made, and there was no turning back. What the future held for her was uncertain, but for Adam it was yet another beginning in the life he had chosen.

Adam produced a bunch of keys from his pocket and, after running his fingers over them, he selected one. He had come to rely vastly on his sense of touch since she had met him, and it was something she was proud to have been able to teach him. Kim watched in silence as he ran his hand over the door to find the keyhole before inserting the key in the lock. It was something he had not tried before, and there was an unmistakable look of triumph on his face when the door swung open.

Kim was not sure what she had expected as she hesitantly followed Adam inside, but she had been unprepared for the stylishly furnished interior of the penthouse. Despite the total disorder and layers of dust, the living-room was tastefully furnished, the colour scheme ranging from cream to various shades of blue, with carpets wall to wall. Built-in shelves, stretching from ceiling to floor, displayed an odd assortment of delicate china, and acted as a room divider. Beyond this was the dining-room, Kim noticed as her keen glance swept over everything.

'I must apologise, Kim,' Adam muttered, slightly embarrassed. 'The place most probably looks a mess. I was wallowing in self-pity before I left here.'

She could no longer ignore the empty beer cans and empty whisky bottles lying about, and she raised straight dark eyebrows above humorous green eyes. 'To be quite honest, it looks as though you were wallowing in booze,' she laughed briefly. 'You must have had a roaring time!'

'Yes, well . . . we'll clean it up later,' he grinned at her unashamedly. 'Let me show you the rest of the place.'

It was the first time Kim had ever been in a penthouse

and it was larger than she had imagined. The kitchen was comfortably spacious, with all the modern appliances a woman could want, with a serving hatch through to the dining-room. The study, with its walls lined with bookshelves, an enormous desk and comfortable leather chairs, led directly off the living-room, and the rest of the penthouse consisted of a spare bedroom and bathroom for his guests, as well as the main bedroom with an adjoining bathroom.

'This will be our room,' he said as they entered, 'and . . . wait a minute!' He caught at her arm and drew her to his side. 'There are two single beds in here.'

'So there are,' Kim acknowledged demurely, her amused glance directed at the twin beds with their serviceable bedspreads in disarray, as if Adam had slept on them alternately without bothering to get beneath the blankets. 'And very comfortable they look too,' she added mischievously.

'I've got a job for you to do first thing Monday morning, and no later than that, my girl,' he said decisively, his hand moving to her shoulder and turning her to face him. 'You're to go into town to buy a double bed, is that clear?'

'But what are we to do with these lovely beds?' she asked protestingly and with mock innocence.

'Trade them in. Sell them. Throw them out the window.'

'But, Adam——'

'Kim, I think I must be old-fashioned,' he remarked sternly as he pulled her into his arms. 'I want to go to sleep each night with my wife in my arms. Am I being unreasonable?'

Kim blushed becomingly. 'No.'

'You're lovely, Kim,' he said at length, burying his lips against the silky warmth of her neck. 'So soft and warm, and you fit so perfectly into my arms.'

Her senses swam as his hard mouth found hers and his hands were deliciously warm and exciting against her skin beneath her sweater. She loved him desperately, with a hungry yearning for his admission of love, but despite his muttered endearments, love was never mentioned.

'Adam,' she gasped against his lips, trying to ward off his advances. 'I should be making lunch and getting the place cleaned up.'

'It can wait, can't it?' he whispered urgently, moulding her body to his in a way that sent intoxicating flames of desire leaping through her veins. 'Can't it?' he repeated the question demandingly.

'Yes. Oh, yes,' she agreed bemusedly, unable to fight against the emotions he had aroused within her. What did it matter that lunch had to be prepared, that the penthouse had to be tidied and that layers of dust had to be dispensed with? It could wait, as Adam had suggested.

Adam's penthouse was in a building overlooking the beach-front, and from the rooftop Kim had a breathtaking view of the sea and the picturesque coastline. Behind her the mountain towered out above the tall buildings as if to prove its superiority. Adam came and stood beside her, lifting his face towards the sun and sniffing the air.

'I always thought the smell of the sea air was so wonderful from here, but it's become rather insipid after living at Heron's Bay for so long,' he remarked disappointedly.

'One can't always have everything the way one wants it,' she pointed out gently.

'Wise little Kim,' he mocked, tugging at her hair. 'What is it that's keeping you out here so long?'

'I was thinking——' she began, glancing about her speculatively. 'With a few flower boxes and several comfortable deck chairs, this could become a splendid retreat when the weather is as perfect as it is today.'

'Perhaps it would be a good idea to exploit these plans of yours while I'm at work,' he agreed with a measure of seriousness. 'It will give you something to do.'

'I might just do that, Adam,' she threatened as they entered the living-room through the sliding doors.

Bill Stewart paid them a visit on the Sunday afternoon as he had promised. He was obviously accustomed to letting himself in, for neither Adam nor Kim knew that he had arrived until they heard him call, 'Anyone home?'

'Yes, we're here in the study,' Kim replied delightedly. 'I'm helping Adam get his books sorted out.'

Bill sauntered into the study, his hazel eyes dancing with mischief. 'I thought I would be in time for tea.'

'But you are,' Kim told him swiftly. 'The kettle is on.'

'Good,' he grinned, glancing at the pile of books on the floor. 'Need any help?'

Adam frowned slightly. 'Well, if you don't mind lending a hand, then Kim could make the tea which I've been promised for the past hour.'

'Oh, dear,' Bill muttered in mock despair as Kim escaped to the kitchen. 'I knew I shouldn't have offered!'

'You'll get nothing for nothing in this place, Bill. Not with Kim around,' Adam informed him with a touch of wry humour. 'She's a slavedriver.'

'I heard that remark, and I object!' Kim shouted from the kitchen as she hurriedly made the tea and set the tray.

Bill deliberately raised his voice a pitch. 'Isn't there a saying about those who listen at keyholes hearing nothing good of themselves?'

Kim realised that they were purposely raising their voices so that she would hear them, and she replied on cue. 'I wasn't listening at the keyhole, and if the two of you aren't careful you won't get tea at all.'

'We'd better behave, Bill,' Adam warned. 'When she speaks in that tone of voice she can become vicious enough to do just as she says.'

'I'm beginning to think that the two of you don't like me,' she remarked teasingly as she entered the study with a laden tray. 'Oh, well, perhaps these freshly baked scones will mellow you a little.'

'Kim, my dear, you are a marvellous creature!' Adam exclaimed, dropping several books on to his desk and facing her innocently.

'Hear, hear!' Bill echoed dramatically.

'Now I'm thoroughly suspicious,' she told them abruptly, glancing from one to the other. 'What do the two of you want?'

'Well, I was hoping for an invitation to dinner,' Bill replied instantly, his hazel eyes dancing with mirth. 'And you, Adam?'

Adam appeared unperturbed. 'I was just hoping to get dinner at all.'

'You're both hopeless,' Kim laughed as she placed

the tray on the desk and started pouring. 'Bill, you're invited to dinner, and you, Adam, shall have the crumbs off my plate if you behave.'

'See what I meant about being vicious?' Adam gestured knowingly towards Bill.

It was quite some time before they settled down to a more serious discussion, and it was Bill who touched on the subject of transport for Adam to and from the centre.

'If Adam agrees, then I could drive him to the Institute in the mornings and fetch him again in the evenings,' Kim intervened. 'It would at least give me something to do.'

'Sounds like a good idea to me,' Bill remarked, glancing questioningly at Adam. 'What do you think, Adam?'

Adam hesitated briefly before replying and, for one brief moment, Kim feared that he would reject her offer. 'If Kim doesn't mind travelling backwards and forwards each day, then I have no objections.'

Relieved that he had accepted her offer, Kim left them alone when it became apparent that Bill wanted to discuss the work with Adam, and she kept herself occupied in the kitchen preparing dinner. Fortunately she had thought to bring meat and vegetables from the cottage, or they might have been stranded with nothing to eat except several tins of sardines she had discovered in the kitchen cupboard. She had managed to obtain fresh bread, as well as milk, butter and eggs from the delicatessen only a block away, and this would have to last until she could do some shopping the following day.

After dinner that evening Bill seemed reluctant to

leave, and Kim blessed him for it when she answered the doorbell shortly after eight to admit Ursula Bennett. With no more than a cursory glance at Kim, she swept past her, leaving behind a waft of expensive perfume and an excellent view of her backbone where her dress plunged to her waist. Kim closed the door and followed more slowly. Ursula Bennett was a vision of beauty from her platinum blonde head down to the fragile-looking silver sandals on her feet. With her gossamer blue dress swirling about her knees with every movement, she looked as though she had just that minute stepped out of a fashion magazine, making Kim painfully aware of her well-worn sweater and comfortable slacks.

'Darling,' she purred, hovering over Adam after she was forced to acknowledge Kim's existence while Adam made the introduction. 'It's about time you came back. It's been simply awful without you, and I can't tell you how pleased I was to hear that Bill had managed to persuade you to come out of hiding.'

Come out of hiding, indeed! Kim thought indignantly, holding her breath as she sensed a growing tension in Adam.

'I'm afraid you're giving me credit for something I don't deserve, Ursula,' Bill remarked dryly. 'It's Adam's wife you have to thank.'

'Oh, really?' Her grey eyes were like icicles licking against Kim's skin, and she shivered. This woman was her enemy, and she made no effort to hide the fact.

'Yes,' Bill continued calmly. 'Without her support my pleas would have been futile.'

This statement obviously displeased Ursula, but she shrugged it off prettily and moved towards the vacant seat beside Adam on the sofa which Kim had occupied until her arrival. Realising her intention, Bill led her nonchalantly towards a vacant chair beside his own. This increased Ursula's displeasure considerably, but Kim gained a new respect for Bill Stewart. She refused Kim's tentative offer of something to drink, and there was undisguised fury in her eyes as Kim resumed her seat beside Adam.

Adam had remained comparatively silent throughout this discourse, almost as if he were assimilating the shock of Ursula's sudden appearance as well as the extent of his feelings for her. It was not difficult for Kim to understand why Adam had found Ursula so attractive. There was not a hair out of place on her beautiful head, not a flaw on her creamy skin, and her voluptuous body was seductive enough without any further efforts on her part. Her clear grey eyes were intelligent, though chilling in their appraisal of Kim, but they came alive subtly when they rested on Adam. She wanted him, Kim realised with sudden clarity, and she would stop at nothing to get him.

'I believe you're to be my personal assistant, Ursula,' Adam remarked casually, but by the set of his jaw Kim knew that his tenseness had not evaporated.

'Who else knows your work better than I do?' she replied, the distinct purr back in her voice. 'I was the logical choice, seeing that we'd worked together so closely in the past.'

Kim glanced warily at Bill, but he smiled reassuringly. Would he be her ally in a time of need? she wondered curiously.

Ursula wanted to talk shop, but this time it was Adam who stopped her decisively with, 'I don't think we should talk about work this evening. It's not fair on Kim.'

'You're not a scientist, then?' she asked, giving Kim the full benefit of her stony glance while knowing the answer to her subtle question.

'No, she's not,' Adam replied abruptly. 'Thank God,' he added in a voice which was barely perceptible to Kim's own ears, and her heart leapt with the knowledge that science was no recommendation with Adam.

To Kim's relief, Ursula did not stay long. She had arrived, made her impact on them all, and then announced that she was departing. As they rose to their feet, she placed a possessive hand on Adam's arm and delivered her parting shot. 'I'll pick you up in the morning, darling. It's on my way.'

Kim stared after her in dismay as she swept through the door and into the lift. 'Well, that takes care of your transport problem, doesn't it?' she said abruptly, unable to hide the bitterness in her voice.

Both men turned then to face her, but Adam was the first to react by placing an arm about her waist and pulling her hard against his side. 'It's perhaps a sensible solution,' he said carefully. 'As Ursula said, it's on her way. She has to pass Sea Point on her way from Camps Bay.'

'That's true, of course,' Kim acknowledged, but not without a certain amount of reluctance.

Adam's hand tightened on her waist before he released her. 'What about making some coffee?'

It was an instruction, not merely a suggestion, but Kim was thankful for the opportunity to be alone for a few minutes to gather her scattered wits about her. She moved about the kitchen, doing what she had to quite mechanically while her mind roamed elsewhere. She had met Ursula Bennett sooner than she had expected, and for the first time in her life she had acquired an enemy. If war was to be declared openly between them, Kim knew she would not stand a chance. Ursula was beautiful and clever, and they were two valuable weapons which Kim did not possess.

When she returned to the living-room some moments later, she caught the tail end of the conversation as Bill said with some urgency, 'You'll have to be careful, Adam.'

Be careful of what? she kept wondering throughout the rest of the evening. Was Bill referring to the work, or Ursula Bennett? She presumed there would be a certain amount of danger involved in Adam's work, but would it necessitate a warning from Bill? If, however, he was referring to Ursula, then Kim could understand the reason for Bill's remark, but what had Adam said that could have instigated it?

After Bill left that evening, Kim took a long, hard look at herself in the mirror, and what she saw did nothing to bolster her confidence. Russet-coloured hair hanging thick and straight down her back; large, anxious green eyes beneath straight dark eyebrows; a small nose and a pointed chin, with a generous mouth and high cheekbones that were inclined to develop hollows beneath them when she was tired. It was not an unattractive face, but not the kind that would launch a thousand ships; not like Ursula's. The rest of her appearance left much to be desired, she thought despairingly as she continued her critical observation of herself. Her breasts were too small and her waist too thin, and when she walked there was none of that flowing grace with which Ursula had swept in and out of the penthouse that evening.

'Aren't you coming to bed?' Adam asked impatiently.

'Just coming,' she sighed, turning away from her despairing image in the mirror and slipping into the bed beside him. On Adam's instructions she had pushed the two beds close together so that he could at least hold her hand if he wished. She snapped off the light and lay staring into the darkness for some time before she was forced to remark, 'She's very beautiful, isn't she?'

'I presume you mean Ursula?'

'Yes.' Kim held her breath as she waited for his affirmative reply.

'Ursula is one of the most beautiful women I've ever seen,' he said at length, not realising that he was twisting the knife deeper into her heart. 'She always reminded me of a cool lake in a scorching desert.'

'A frozen lake, more likely, with ice cubes where her heart ought to be,' Kim thought cattishly as sheer unadulterated jealousy surged through her. 'Why did you never marry her?' she asked.

'I don't know. I suppose I just somehow never got around to asking her.'

'Would you, if you'd been free now, have asked her to marry you?' Kim continued, her pulse throbbing with agonising precision against her temples.

'That question is irrelevant,' Adam pointed out irritably. 'I *am* married, and there's no question of marrying Ursula. Why should I want to marry her when I have you, my beautiful Kim?'

'But, Adam, I'm not beautiful,' she protested, silent tears choking her.

Adam moved suddenly beside her. 'Hold my hand,

Kim,' he instructed harshly, and as his fingers gripped hers he continued: 'To me you are beautiful, Kim, and I refuse to believe that anyone with a nature such as yours could be ugly.' He leaned over her unexpectedly and kissed her hard and convincingly on the mouth. 'Now stop talking or I shall never get to sleep.'

Her fears momentarily lulled, but not entirely stilled, Kim drifted off into an easy sleep where reality could not touch her for a few hours.

Adam was awake earlier than usual that Monday morning. It was restless energy combined with tension, he confessed when Kim awoke to find that he had already bathed and shaved, and was going through his wardrobe in search of something to wear. She watched him closely for some minutes, but when he finally selected a blue shirt and dark green suit, she had to intervene.

'You can't wear that, the colours will clash,' she told him calmly as she slipped out of bed and went to his aid, selecting a dark brown suit and cream-coloured shirt, with a tie to match. She also placed his shoes and socks beside the bed where she knew he would find them.

Leaving Adam to dress himself, Kim went through to the bathroom and could not help smiling as she looked about her. Very few women would walk into a bathroom after their husbands had emerged, to find everything so orderly, but Adam's blindness had enforced this tidiness if he wished to find what he wanted without effort. His electric razor and after-shave lotion was placed neatly on the shelf, and his damp towel was draped across the towel rack. Nothing was out of place.

Later, when Adam sat down to breakfast, Kim stared at him in astonishment. In the unfamiliar clothes, with his hair brushed severely into place, he had become the distinguished stranger she had seen only once before on their wedding day. This was Dr Adam Granger, scientist, a fact which had not made much impression on her before, but it was something she would have difficulty in ignoring in the future. Something close to fear lodged in her stomach. They were suddenly worlds apart; moving in different spheres. If it had not been for his blindness, they might never have met, and, even now, it was only his blindness and her understanding that bound them together. She loved him, but would that be enough for a man like Adam?

'Have I lost you somewhere, Kim?' Adam asked suddenly, interrupting her thoughts.

'No, I'm still here,' she laughed hollowly, placing his plate of eggs and bacon in front of him and putting the toast rack within easy reach. 'I was thinking.'

'What about?'

Kim cupped her chin in her hands and watched him eat in silence for a moment, marvelling at his adeptness. 'I was thinking about you. You look so different. You *are* different.'

'I suppose it's the clothes,' he suggested, helping himself to another slice of toast. 'There was never any need to dress other than casually at Heron's Bay. That's what makes it such a splendid retreat.'

'It's not only the clothes,' she remarked thoughtfully, a frown appearing between her eyes. 'There's an aura about you this morning that's strange. It's almost as if you've become another person.'

Adam put down his knife and fork abruptly and

extended his hand, palm upwards, towards her. 'Who am I, Kim?' he asked as she placed her hand hesitantly in his.

'At the moment you're Dr Adam Granger to the very last detail,' she replied, not quite understanding.

Adam shook his head impatiently. 'Let me put it this way. What am I . . . to you?'

Kim met his blue gaze and her treacherous heart missed a beat. 'You're . . . my husband.'

'Exactly,' he nodded, releasing her hand, 'and don't forget it.'

The burning desire to say, 'Adam, I love you,' made her lean back weakly in her chair, closing her eyes as she bit back the words that were spilling from her heart and hovering on her lips. This was not the time, nor the place, and Adam would not appreciate the mention of the word 'love'. It was a word he had silently and cynically made taboo in their relationship.

Kim accompanied Adam down in the lift and while she waited with him in the foyer, she helped him check through the items in his briefcase once more before he left. Ursula arrived with a flourish in her red Mustang soon after eight, stepping out on to the pavement with polished grace, and looking as though she was about to partake in a fashion parade.

'I'm not late, am I?' she purred up at Adam, completely ignoring Kim's presence. 'The traffic was rather heavy.'

Adam assured her that they had not been waiting long and then, to Ursula's obvious vexation, he drew Kim into his arms and kissed her thoroughly on the lips.

'Don't forget that you have some shopping to do this morning,' he reminded her with the old mocking grin, and she blushed furiously as she realised that he was referring to the purchase of a double bed. 'You'll find a signed cheque on the dressing table.'

With a last brief kiss he released her, and allowed Ursula to lead him to her car. Kim stood staring after them, suddenly lost, and with a taste of loneliness to come. She would miss Adam, and the times they had spent together. She would like to think she had contributed towards his total independence, preparing him as one would a child for school. Now he was on his own, with Ursula to complete the progress.

Kim turned and entered the lift with a distasteful grimace flicking across her sensitive face. It would be foolish to ignore the fact that Ursula was a threat to their happiness, but there was absolutely nothing Kim could do about it.

CHAPTER SEVEN

LONELINESS became the essence of Kim's life while Adam spent hours at the Institute, often not arriving home until long after dinner. The evenings Kim hated most were those when Adam and Ursula spent the evening behind the closed door of his study while they went over the paper work of the project. Ursula would arrive with Adam just before dinner, and Kim would be left with no alternative but to invite her to join them. After dinner Kim would find herself making endless trips to and from the kitchen to supply them with the liquid refreshment they required. There never appeared to be any time to spend alone with Adam.

Ursula was always there, forcing Kim into the background with her scientific knowledge and, Kim suspected, using the project as an excuse to claim Adam's attention at all times.

Adam adapted to this new situation with surprising swiftness. There were a few minor incidents at work which had angered him, but, after his own initial nervousness and that of his colleagues, everything seemed to go smoothly.

Nothing else existed beyond the project for Adam, and although Kim tried to understand and accept this, it was a little frightening to discover that her husband was becoming a stranger to her in every way. Bill Stewart became aware of Kim's increasing loneliness soon after their arrival in Cape Town and, whenever possible, he paid her a visit and kept her company while Adam and Ursula were occupied in the study.

Kim refused to hire a servant. Doing the household chores, she insisted, was one way of occupying herself. When she had time to spare, she would go for long walks along the promenade, and occasionally she drove into town to do the odd bit of shopping. This was how she spent her time during the remainder of the winter, and well into the spring.

Bill arrived one evening and found Kim pacing the living-room floor. 'All alone?' he asked with raised eyebrows.

'No.' She gestured towards the closed door. 'Adam and Ursula are in the study, poring over papers that look terribly complicated, and sound frightening.'

Bill frowned angrily. 'I think it's a damn shame that Adam should treat you like this. You've only been married . . . how long?'

'Six months,' Kim replied, forcing her unwilling lips into a smile.

'Six months!' he exclaimed, his red hair flaming in the lamplight. 'He behaves as if you've been married for years! Adam has always taken his job seriously, but this time he seems to have gone beyond the limit.'

'Bill, I'm frightened,' Kim admitted suddenly after a brief silence, her hair veiling her troubled expression as she lowered her head. 'There's no one else I can talk to . . . except you.'

He smiled encouragingly. 'I'm a good listener.'

Kim bit her lip and hesitated briefly. It was difficult to talk about the things that disturbed her deeply, but, despite her stubborn independence, this was a problem she could not solve on her own. 'You must have noticed that the relationship between Ursula and myself is rather strained,' she began tentatively, taking a deep breath before making her next statement. 'Ursula resents the fact that I'm married to Adam. She considers him her property.'

Bill lit a cigarette and blew the smoke towards the ceiling. 'That may be so, but there's absolutely nothing she can do about it, is there?'

'Except to force us apart.'

Bill sustained her troubled glance for a long time before asking quite calmly, 'You're not going to let her succeed, are you?'

Kim sighed dejectedly, letting her hair swing back on to her shoulders. 'I don't see how I'm going to avoid it. She has all the weapons on her side. She spends all day with him at work, and almost every evening. She's beautiful, intelligent, on Adam's wavelength as they say, and she also has the added advantage of once being

114

his . . . girl-friend.' Kim steadied her trembling lips. 'If this was a competition, then I wouldn't stand a chance, and Ursula's going all out to get him.'

'Adam could have married Ursula if he'd wanted to, but he didn't,' Bill pointed out. 'He married you.'

'You might as well know, Bill, that Adam married me at a time when he thought he no longer had a future as a scientist. He was in a dreadful state when I met him, physically and mentally. He needed help and guidance, and I happened to be the only one who could give it to him. Our marriage started in the most unorthodox fashion, as a business arrangement, until such time that other arrangements could be made.' Kim bit her lip. 'Does this shock you?'

'No, it's typical of Adam.'

'Well, eventually we discovered that we . . . liked each other enough to make our marriage a real one, and we were happy. But that was at Heron's Bay, without the disturbing influence of Ursula Bennett to bring back memories of what could have been.'

'Has Adam's behaviour towards you changed?'

Kim shook her head firmly. 'No . . . except that our conversations are now spiced with "Ursula says", and "Ursula suggests".'

Bill scowled down at the remainder of his cigarette before crushing it into an ashtray. 'You shouldn't allow her to take over Adam's life so completely.'

'How do you suggest I prevent it?' Her eyes turned involuntarily towards the study door. 'Ursula has a perfectly valid reason for spending so much time with Adam, and I don't know enough about their work to contradict this.'

'There are other methods of making Adam more

aware of you,' Bill stated reflectively. 'You're far too retiring about the whole situation. You should go out and beat her at her own game.'

Kim's lips curled with amusement. 'How?'

'Do you have money of your own?'

'Yes . . . as well as a generous allowance from Adam which I rarely use. Why?'

'Well, my dear Kim, you're going to go out and buy yourself some stunning clothes. Get rid of your slacks and sweaters, and dowdy little dresses. What you need are some fantastic creations that will do justice to your figure.' Bill's glance swept over her critically. 'The next thing you've got to do is have your hair cut slightly shorter, and styled to suit your new image. Lastly, a visit to a beautician would do wonders. They could tell you what make-up to use, and demonstrate how it should be applied to gain the best results.'

'You make me sound terribly gauche,' Kim laughed self-consciously, but her interest was aroused.

'Heaven help me that I should give you that impression, Kim,' he said quickly, with a seriousness that sat comically on his usually merry face. 'To me you're fine just as you are, but if you're going to wage war against Ursula, then you'll need every weapon you can lay your hands on.'

'What's the use, Bill?' she sighed defeatedly after a brief moment of thought. 'Adam is blind.'

'That's where I come in,' he told her.

'You?'

'Yes, my dear.' His eyes were dancing with merriment. 'I shall start by flashing compliments around when Adam is about, and I shall go quite lyrical in my detailed description of what you're wearing, and so forth. Another thing,' he continued after a brief pause, 'start wearing perfume. Get yourself something with a delicate fragrance that will intrigue Adam, and which is not as overpowering as the kind Ursula normally uses.'

Kim caught her thumbnail between her teeth and considered Bill's suggestions quite seriously. 'You make it all sound so exciting, but will it work?'

Bill raised his hands in the air in mock despair. 'If it doesn't, we could always pretend, as a last resort, that I've been smitten by you. That should make Adam sit up and take notice.'

'Poor Adam,' she said simply, envisaging his confusion if such drastic measures had to be taken.

Bill gazed at her intently. 'You love him very much, don't you?'

'I love him so much that I'm willing to try anything to ensure that Ursula remains in the past,' she admitted with a touch of aggressiveness that surprised even herself.

'Good girl!' he smiled, clasping her hand swiftly. 'Do as I say and leave the rest to Uncle Bill.'

Almost a week had passed before Kim plucked up enough courage to do as Bill had suggested. She was going to make herself as attractive as possible for a man who would never be able to see her. It was both ridiculous and exciting, as well as incredibly sad.

At an exclusive boutique in the city she selected an entire new wardrobe that took her breath away, and made a sizeable dent in her allowance. At this stage, Kim was beyond caring about the final cost of this unusual operation. She had been dazzled by the beauty of those expensive garments which would certainly compare favourably with anything Ursula chose to wear.

Her next stop was at the hairdresser, and she stared in dismay at the ostentatiously dressed man who approached her. Jacques, as he introduced himself in a practised French accent, wore tight-fitting scarlet trousers, a silky lilac shirt, and a yellow scarf tied about his neck. His hair was long, sleek, and well-groomed, and he gestured delicately with his slender hands as he raved about the colour of her hair, but he shook his head sadly at the neglect. Kim's anger rose sharply, but subsided swiftly as he began to explain. He would cut and shape her hair just slightly before the shampoo, after which he would treat her scalp and hair, with something unpronounceable, before styling it in a way she could comfortably manage on her own.

Jacques set to work with the scissors and comb, and followed this up with the shampoo and scalp massage. As the minutes slipped by, a new Kim emerged that made her stare at herself in the mirror with utter amazement. Her hair barely touched her shoulders, the ends curling upwards slightly, and looking soft and bouncy with every movement she made, while in the light overhead it appeared to be emitting sparks of fire.

'*Magnifique!*' Jacques exclaimed delightedly as he stood to one side admiring the result. 'Now, I think, I shall send our beautician to Madam.'

Another hour slipped by—an hour in which Kim was instructed in the art of using make-up to its best advantage without appearing unnatural. Kim, quite bedazzled by the stunning results, went home with her newly acquired make-up kit, and a quivering excitement to test Bill and Ursula's reactions.

At home, alone in her bedroom, Kim stared at herself in the mirror once more and could not believe what she saw. She was still not beautiful, she acknowledged to herself, but attractive . . . yes! Someone Adam need not be ashamed of introducing as his wife. Her hair was lustrous and soft to the touch, her green eyes large and luminous, the naturally thick lashes adding a touch of mystery, and her lips delicately shaded to give a natural effect. The high cheekbones were toned down slightly, no longer giving her that gaunt look she so despised. The final touch of her new appearance was one of the exquisite creations she had bought, and she had to admit that her slender, almost boyish figure appeared alluringly feminine as the soft, apricot-coloured material clung gently to breasts and waist, to hang in cloud-like folds about her shapely legs.

Would Bill approve? she wondered curiously before an agonising realisation overwhelmed her. It was not Bill's approval that she craved, but Adam's! And Adam shall never be able to voice his opinion, or give his approval.

Kim suppressed an involuntary shiver and shook herself free of these disturbing thoughts. After taking a last critical look at herself in the full-length mirror, she went through to Adam's study and telephoned Bill.

'Come over this evening and have dinner with us,' she said without preamble when Bill's voice came over the line. 'Adam and Ursula will be here as well. Adam mentioned this morning that he would be bringing work home.'

'Thank you, Kim. I could do with a decent meal,' he teased.

'Bill . . . come a little early. I would like your opinion of the new me before they arrive.'

'I'll be there, Kim, and looking forward to it.'

For some time after she had replaced the receiver, Kim sat there in Adam's chair staring thoughtfully at the blotter before her. What was happening to her? She had always been so sure of herself, completely unconcerned about the fact that she was not beautiful. Yet, suddenly, it had become the most important thing in her life to be beautiful and attractive for Adam, something which made little difference to him in his sightless world. He thought her beautiful, but she was not, although she could no longer deny that, with the right clothes and accessories, she was reasonably attractive. Would this be enough to make Ursula admit defeat? Or would it merely make her more determined in her efforts to hold Adam?

Kim sighed heavily as she went through to the kitchen to start the dinner. From the first moment she had heard Ursula's name mentioned, she had been aware of an element of fear. Now, having met her, Ursula had become a threat to her happiness, a threat and a challenge which Kim could not ignore if she wanted to remain Adam's wife.

Shortly before Bill arrived, Kim went through to the bedroom to touch up her make-up and to experiment with the perfume in the fragile-looking bottle. She had hesitated to purchase the perfume because of the shattering price, but she succumbed to the sales lady's persuasive comments that the perfume could very easily have been made specially for her.

It was just as well that she had left her allowance

practically untouched during the past months, Kim thought nervously, for her shopping expedition that morning had left her with nothing worth mentioning, and she shuddered to think what Adam would have to say about it if he should find out. It had all been fun, but had it been the right thing to do?

The front door bell rang insistently and there was no further time to ponder about the wiseness of her actions. Bill had arrived, and she would soon know whether her efforts had been a success.

'I can't believe it!' Bill exclaimed in surprise as she let him in. He glanced at her critically with narrowed eyes. 'You're beautiful, Kim.'

'Don't flatter me, Bill,' she warned anxiously as she led the way to the living-room. 'Just tell me the truth. I can take it.'

'I've already told you the truth, Kim.'

'But Ursula——'

'Ursula has that cool kind of beauty that intrigues and excites men, but leaves them unconvinced,' he interrupted earnestly, turning Kim to face him. 'Your beauty is warm and vibrant, as well as eye-catching. It also comes from within, with the capacity to make a man wear out the soles of his shoes in the process of gaining your favour. If I were Adam, I would be terrified to lose you.'

'Oh, Bill,' she whispered tremulously, her eyes brimming with unshed tears. 'You sound so convincing.'

'No tears now, or you'll spoil the beautiful job you've done on those fantastic eyes of yours,' he warned quickly, smiling down at her warmly. 'All right?'

'All right,' Kim laughed shakily, pulling herself

together drastically.

Bill sniffed appreciatively. 'And I love that perfume. It's soft and feminine, and it suits you perfectly.'

'That's what the sales lady said,' she said abruptly, regaining her composure and turning towards the kitchen. 'You'd better pour yourself a drink while I see to the dinner. Adam won't be home for a few minutes yet.'

'Can I pour you something as well?'

'I'll have a small sherry, please, Bill.'

Kim took a deep breath to steady her nerves once she reached the kitchen, while Bill found glasses and poured their drinks. It was no use trying to deny that she was terribly nervous. She felt very much like a child dressed up for her first party, and not knowing quite what to expect or how to behave.

'Here's your drink,' said Bill, coming up behind her and handing her the glass of sherry. 'Do you mind if I join you here in the kitchen? The pleasant aroma of the dinner, combined with this drink, is enough to whet my appetite.'

Kim sipped at her drink and placed the glass on the table, staring thoughtfully down into the dark red liquid. 'Bill, there's something else I have always wanted to ask you.'

'Ask away, Kim.'

She chewed nervously at her lip. 'I know that Adam didn't want to see anyone after his accident, but, if Ursula was so keen on him, then why didn't she ever try to visit him?'

'She did see him once while he was in hospital, but she became so tactless and over emotional that Adam refused to see her again.' Bill heaved a sigh. 'As a matter of fact, he left instructions that he wanted to see no one, and none of us have ever dared to thwart his wishes. Not even Ursula.'

'Was she very upset when you told her about me?'

'I thought she was going to burst a blood-vessel!'

His boyish grin told her just how much he had enjoyed passing on that information, and she burst out laughing. She could quite easily visualise Ursula's reaction to the news that the man she wanted belonged to another, and it could not have been a pretty sight, she decided unhappily.

The sound of a key being turned in the lock of the front door drew their attention. 'Kim!'

'That's Adam,' she said unnecessarily, her face sobering instantly as she hurried from the kitchen to greet him. 'Bill is here with me. I invited him to dinner.'

Adam removed his dark glasses before opening his arms, and Kim walked straight into them, receiving his kiss with more enthusiasm than usual because she knew that Ursula was watching. It was only as Adam released her that she glanced surreptitiously in Ursula's direction and noticed the look of utter surprise that kept her adversary immobile and silent.

'There's something different about you,' Adam remarked with a frown, not releasing his hold on her hands.

'I'll say there's something different about her!' Bill exclaimed with more enthusiasm than Kim thought necessary. 'I've never seen Kim look so beautiful, Adam.'

'Really?' There was a faint touch of amusement on Adam's lean face, and Kim felt her cheeks grow hot.

'Yes, old man,' Bill continued, obviously enjoying

himself in this new role. 'She's wearing the most beautiful silk creation I've ever seen. It clings in all the right places, and the colour is just perfect.'

'Colour?'

'It's a sort of apricot colour, I would say, and it blends with the colour of her hair when the light catches it.'

'For goodness' sake, Bill, you sound like a walking advertisement!' Ursula snapped irritably, recovering from the momentary shock of discovering that Adam's wife presented more danger than she had originally visualised.

Bill drew himself up to his full height, and cast Ursula an indignant glance. 'If Kim were *my* wife, I would certainly want to advertise the fact. Besides, Adam likes to know occasionally what his wife looks like. Not so, Adam?' he asked confidently, turning back to the tall, lean man who stood listening to this interchange with a deepening amusement.

'I'm much obliged to you, Bill,' said Adam.

'Bill, will you pour them something to drink while I get the dinner on the table?' Kim intervened quickly, managing to release her hands from Adam's before escaping to the kitchen.

It had all been very flattering, but enough was enough. Her cheeks were so hot that it felt as though they were on fire and, taking Ursula's cool and sophisticated behaviour into consideration, it was a sign that she lacked confidence. To thwart Ursula's attempts to ruin her marriage, she would have to display more confidence in herself, Kim told herself angrily, straightening her back in preparation for the continuation of the ensuing battle.

Dinner was not entirely a success that evening. Ursula insisted on claiming Adam's attention on matters which she knew Kim could not contribute to, and Bill was just as persistent at intervening, in order to bring the conversation round to a subject which could involve Kim. It was all very deliberate, and rather unpleasant. The dinner table had become a battle field where cunning played a major role, and Kim sent countless glances in Adam's direction to observe his reactions, but he was either completely oblivious of the various undercurrents, or exceptionally clever at hiding his true feelings.

Kim planned her own distasteful strategy in silence. As she served the different courses, she made a point of touching Adam, either by placing a hand on his shoulder, or by running her hand casually down the back of his head. It was a show of possessiveness Kim was rather ashamed of, but it had the desired effect, for at one stage Adam's hand found hers and clasped it where it lay on the table close to him, and he held it for some time before relinquishing his hold.

At this unaccustomed display of affection, Bill sat back in his chair and smiled with satisfaction, while Ursula's eyes shot icicles at Kim. By the determined set of her lips, Kim knew that she would not admit defeat easily. This was merely the beginning of the battle which had been brewing for some time.

After dinner they returned to the living-room, and Kim purposely seated herself on the arm of Adam's chair, which further annoyed Ursula. It was not long before Ursula played her usual trump card, but this time without much success.

'Come on, Adam darling,' she purred invitingly.

'It's time we got down to work.'

Bill shot Kim a glance that said quite clearly: 'Over my dead body will you allow her to drag Adam away!' but Adam, too, seemed rather reluctant to closet himself in the study with the delectable blonde.

'Not this evening, Ursula. This is one night the work can remain in my briefcase where it belongs,' he said firmly, placing an arm about Kim's slim waist and drawing her closer. 'Any objections, Kim?'

Kim's heart thumped heavily against her ribs. 'None at all,' she whispered joyously, lowering her head to place her cheek against his dark head just below hers.

Intensely satisfied with the way things were developing, Bill relaxed in his armchair, lit a cigarette, and blew smoke rings into the air. Ursula, on the other hand, seemed at a loss to know how to handle this new situation, and Kim could not help but feel sorry for her. It was the first time she had seen Ursula's confidence shattered, and it was not something she felt inclined to rejoice about. Ursula wanted Adam, and if so, she must love him, Kim thought distractedly. If positions were reversed, would she not feel exactly the same as Ursula and, perhaps, react in precisely the same way?

Ursula did not wait too long before she thanked Kim with chilly politeness for the dinner, and departed with nothing more than a cool nod in Kim's direction as she saw her to the door. Bill remained a while longer to have the coffee Kim had offered to make, before he, too, left for home.

Kim cleared the table and washed the dishes while Adam went through to the bathroom. No matter how much she tried, she could not rid herself of the feeling that she had been persuaded to start something she might yet regret. Ursula was not the kind of person who would show reluctance to fight back, and she could become a venomous adversary. An alarming thought occurred to her. What if Adam actually desired the attention Ursula lavished on him? What if he still cared? Would it not have been more sensible then to have left things as they were?

Kim went through to the bedroom and squeezed a liberal amount of hand lotion into the palm of her hand, massaging it into her skin with unnecessary vigour. If only Adam would talk about Ursula! If only he would make his feelings known to her, Kim thought agitatedly just as Adam emerged from the bathroom with a towel tied about his waist. He seemed to sense her presence and came towards her, looking lean and muscular, with his hair still damp from his shower, and the familiar odour of after-shave lotion still clinging to him.

Standing perfectly still as he approached her, Kim savoured the bitter-sweet delight of knowing that she belonged to Adam completely, even if, at some time in the future, he should wish to terminate their uncertain relationship.

His arms encircled her waist and he drew her unresistingly against him. 'Whatever that perfume is you're wearing, it smells good,' he remarked, nuzzling her neck. 'I like your dress as well. It's so soft and silky,' he continued, running his hands down the length of her body and making her tremble.

'I—I'm glad you like it, Adam.'

He raised his head suddenly, his expression registering a new concern. 'Have I neglected you very much lately?'

'You have.'

'Kim, my dear, please try to understand that I'm working against time.' The pressure of his hands was urgent against her back. 'We have to reach the testing stage of this project before Christmas. Do you realise that this gives me less than two months? If we don't continue working in the way we have, then——'

'Please,' she silenced him with her fingers against his lips. 'Please don't say anything further. I understand, and I'm rather ashamed that I'm the cause of your not working this evening. It was unforgivable of me.'

'You've been rather distracting this evening, but pleasantly so,' he grinned down at her with a hint of mockery. 'I needed the break, Kim. We all did,' he added, lowering his head to claim her lips. 'The dinner was superb, by the way.'

'Thank you very much, kind sir.'

'You've cut your hair,' he said in astonishment as he pushed his fingers through it. 'You have, haven't you?'

'Only a little.'

'You've done something else to it as well, 'he persisted, frowning with concentration, his fingers moving disturbingly through her hair. 'It's curling softly at the ends.'

'Yes,' she admitted, smiling to herself. 'The hairdresser assured me that it made me look quite elegant.'

Adam twisted a strand of hair about his hand and tugged at it gently, the same glimmer of amusement on his face which she had seen earlier that evening. 'Am I right in thinking that this was all done for my benefit?'

'Naturally.' The dark hairs on his chest were soft and springy beneath her fingers. 'Do I ever do anything which isn't for your benefit?'

'Was that why Bill went to such dramatic lengths to

describe what you looked like?'

Kim swallowed with nervous embarrassment. 'You're far too clever, Adam. How did you know?'

'It's chemistry,' he laughed, burying his lips against the hollow in her throat, and sliding his hands possessively over her hips, 'and at this moment there's a chemical reaction between us which is truly delightful.'

Confused and outraged, she struggled against him. 'You're hateful! Let me go!'

'It's too late, Kim,' he declared, mocking her gently as his arms tightened about her. His hard mouth took possession of hers and she fought against the overwhelming desire to surrender. 'You started this, remember,' he murmured eventually against her lips, 'now you have no option but to see it through to the end. You've tantalised me all evening with your fragrant presence, and the subtle invitation in every remark you made. You can't withdraw now.'

The heavy beat of his heart was beneath her fingertips, his lean, hard body compelling and warm against her own.

'I can, and I will,' she stated defiantly, but the defiance in her voice sounded unconvincing to her own ears, and she was incapable of offering any resistance as her zip gave way beneath his strong fingers.

'Why am I fighting it?' she asked herself suddenly as she thrilled to the touch of his warm hands against her skin. Adam needed her. He called it chemistry; she called it love, but it was the only weapon available to her . . . his need, and her love for him.

Long after Adam was asleep, Kim still lay awake with her cheek resting against his shoulder, his cool breath against her forehead. Was this the only way she could hold him? With her body? she wondered unhappily. 'When there is no love,' her father had once told her, 'a man can tire of the physical bondage a woman places on him.' Would Adam eventually tire of her? And when he did, would he turn again to Ursula?

'No!' she groaned aloud, flinging her arm about him and burying her face against his neck. She could not live without him now, or ever. It was unthinkable!

'Kim?' Adam questioned, aroused from his sleep. 'Are you all right?'

'Yes, Adam. I—I was dreaming,' she lied convincingly to reassure him, and his arms went about her instantly, warm and comforting, and safe. Safe for the moment, until those disturbing thoughts returned and became a frightening reality.

'Oh, God,' she prayed silently. 'Don't let anything, or anyone take him away from me. Not now! Not while I love him so!'

CHAPTER EIGHT

CAPE TOWN was experiencing a heatwave just before Christmas that left everyone limp and lethargic as the humidity increased. During the evenings when Adam was home, they spent their time relaxing in deck chairs on the rooftop garden, staring at the stars and revelling in the refreshingly cool breeze that blew up from the sea. It was peaceful just to lie there with the sound of the traffic no more than a faint hum in the background, and a comfortable silence lingering between them.

That evening, as on several other occasions, Adam lay smoking his pipe, the sweet, cloying aroma of the tobacco hovering pleasantly in the air.

Kim observed him in silence, finding pleasure in just letting her glance slide over him. He had shed his jacket and tie, and his shirt sleeves were rolled up to above his elbows, while his shirt buttons were left undone almost down to the belt of his trousers. In the darkness she was only just able to see the dark patch of hair on his muscular chest, his white shirt contrasting heavily with the tan he had acquired by spending as much time as possible in the sun. There was not an ounce of super-fluous fat on him, and at first glance he appeared almost thin, but that lean, hard body was deceptively wiry and muscular. Those slender hands, usually so gentle, could at times be equally ruthless in their strength.

It was Adam who finally broke the companionable silence between them by saying matter-of-factly: 'I hope you don't mind, Kim, but I've invited Ursula to come over on Christmas Day and have dinner with us that evening.'

Anger and disappointment choked her. 'Did you have to ask her?'

'I am rather under an obligation to her, and as she's on her own, I thought it the only decent thing to do.'

'I don't know why you have to feel under an obli-gation to her,' Kim protested hotly. 'She gets paid for the job she's doing.'

'That was uncalled-for,' he rebuked her sharply, and Kim winced inwardly. She had deserved that.

'I'm sorry, but I had hoped that we might be able to spend the day in the country, or that you might like to take a trip out to your parents on the farm.' Her anger simmered as she continued persuasively, 'I've never been there, and——'

'Kim, when will you realise that my father and I live very much our own lives?' Adam interrupted impatiently, removing his pipe from his mouth and knocking the ash into the ashtray beside him.

'But he's your father, and it will be Christmas,' she protested, shocked by his remark. 'I really don't understand you, Adam. If I hadn't telephoned your father some months ago, he would still have been under the impression that we were at Heron's Bay.'

'My father has his new wife, Libby, to think about,' Adam stated bluntly, his expression inscrutable in the darkness. 'It might also interest you to know that, when I lost my sight, he was too busy to pay me a visit in hospital.'

'Perhaps he was busy.'

'Yes, it was shearing time, but if my son . . .'

'Adam, don't hold it against him,' she pleaded swiftly, understanding his feelings, yet doggedly defending his father's actions.

'I don't hold it against him. I merely live my own life and let him get on with his,' he stated with a finality that was forbidding.

'To get back to Christmas Day,' Kim continued with a touch of defiance. 'If you have invited Ursula, then I don't suppose you'll object if I invite Bill?'

'Bill is becoming rather a pain in the neck lately.'

She drew her breath in sharply and snapped: 'So is Ursula!'

'Jealous?'

The air was painfully tense as she swung her feet to the ground and sat facing him. 'Have I reason to be?'

'You're my wife, Kim.'

'I'm amazed that you occasionally remember that,' she said abruptly, her voice heavy with unaccustomed sarcasm.

'And what is that supposed to mean?' There was an ominous sound to his voice in the darkness and Kim trembled involuntarily.

'Oh, Adam, I wish——' She bit back her words, not knowing whether to continue.

'Go on,' he urged calmly. 'You don't usually hesitate to speak your mind.'

'I wish I were more sure of you, and knew exactly where I stood,' she burst out, not caring what interpretation he put on those words.

Adam seemed to be a long time choosing his words, and when he finally spoke, his voice sparked off a chill that grew alarmingly inside her. 'There's nothing in this world today which one can be sure of. The best remedy is to take things as they come.'

'That's a rather cynical observation!'

'It may be cynical, but it's true,' he pointed out, rising to his feet and towering above her, his expression harsh in the dim light coming from the living-room.

'In other words, you don't consider anything to be lasting.'

'No, I don't.'

Kim swallowed convulsively, her voice sounding as though it belonged to someone else. 'Not even our marriage?'

'Especially not our marriage,' Adam replied without hesitation, turning his back on her as he refilled his pipe. 'You may tire of me. I may tire of you. Who knows?'

Shaken to the very depths, Kim rose slowly to her

feet and stared hard at his imposing back through a film of tears. Adam knew her weak spot and when he struck, he struck hard, and obviously with little thought for her feelings. She stood there on trembling limbs, the aching hurt in her heart searing through her with every agonising beat. She was bereft of speech for some considerable time as she struggled to control the violent trembling of her lips.

'I've suddenly seen a side of your nature that appals me, Adam,' she managed at last, forcing the words past the aching lump in her throat. 'You're shallow, and incapable of any of the finer, deeper feelings most people are endowed with. You treat people like garments which can be discarded when they're of no further use to you, and I think you're despicable!'

Adam remained standing with his back turned rigidly towards her, almost as if he had not heard a word she had said, and Kim felt the most overwhelming urge to shake him violently. Not trusting herself to remain a minute longer in his presence, she stormed inside, shaking with rage, and with only one thought in mind: He and Ursula deserved each other with their twisted, cynical, scientific attitude towards life.

For the first time that night, Kim went to bed before Adam, pretending to be asleep when he leaned over her, whispering her name softly. Despite her anger, she could not prevent her heart from leaping wildly at his nearness when, after a few suffocating seconds, the tips of his fingers lightly brushed her eyelids to make sure that she was actually sleeping. His breath fanned her cheek and, to her surprise, she felt the caressing touch of his lips against her temple before he turned over and switched off the light. Kim lay motionless, hardly daring to breathe as her eyes became accustomed to the darkness.

Adam's callous remarks had hurt her deeply, yet she could not bring herself to remain angry with him. Loving him as much as she did, she could only pity his inability to accept the fact that love actually existed, and that it was not merely a word which was bandied about to appear fashionable.

He stirred restlessly beside her, his hand seeking hers. Kim forced herself to keep her hand lifeless in his clasp, but despite this he seemed satisfied and lay quietly beside her until his deep, regular breathing told her he was asleep. She closed her eyes then and tried to relax, but her conversation with him kept milling through her mind, making her unhappiness a vibrant, living thing that lay heavily in her soul until tiredness washed over it and brought relief in sleep.

Christmas Day was not at all as Kim had planned it. Instead of spending a quiet day alone with Adam and his family, she found herself dancing attendance on Ursula, with Adam and Bill running a close second and third. It was a hot, humid day, that demanded cold meats and carefully prepared salads, with cool, refreshing drinks sipped leisurely throughout the day.

After dinner that evening, Kim felt close to collapse. Ursula's niggling presence had built up a tension within her that stretched her nerves to breaking point. If it had not been for Bill's cheery presence, she would have come close to throttling Ursula on several occasions when she deliberately issued orders which Kim could not avoid obeying. Kim became the maid, seeing to her employer's wishes, and spending more time in the kitchen preparing delicacies than in the company of her guests. All this, of course, gave Ursula more time with Adam, and she used it by oozing charm and flattery that obviously pleased and delighted Adam, for he looked as contented as a cat that had got at the cream, Kim thought fiercely, as she prepared yet another tray of refreshments.

To her surprise, Ursula had managed to tear herself away from Adam's side on this occasion, and she came strolling into the kitchen and stood watching Kim moving about, rinsing glasses and filling them up once more with iced orange juice. Kim's shoulders moved uneasily beneath the silk of her blouse, but she gave no other indication that Ursula's presence disturbed her. What did she want? Kim wondered distractedly. Why this sudden interest in the kitchen?

'The domesticated little wife, aren't you?'

Kim glanced up into cold grey eyes that were sparkling with venom, and laced with obvious mockery. 'I try to make Adam happy.'

'And for how long do you suppose this domesticity will keep him enthralled?' Those crimson lips twisted sardonically, and for some reason Kim was instantly on her guard.

'I don't think I know what you're implying.'

Ursula's perfectly manicured hands gestured expressively as she draped herself elegantly against the dresser. 'Adam has always thrived on intellectual discussions with knowledgeable people on a scientific level. Do you know anything about science?'

Kim fought against the white-hot rage that flared within her, and she warned herself urgently to remain calm. 'No, but Adam and I have not yet reached the point where we find we have nothing to say to each other.'

'What happens when you do?' Ursula smirked.

'I think I shall worry about that when the time comes.'

Ursula's lips twisted cynically. 'You don't like me very much, do you?'

'Is there any reason why I shouldn't like you?' Kim prevaricated, preparing to take the tray of drinks through to the living-room, but one glance in Ursula's direction told her that there was much more on this woman's mind. Kim placed the tray firmly on the kitchen table and turned to face her adversary. 'Ursula, you're obviously trying to tell me something. Why don't you lay your cards on the table, as they say, and do some plain speaking?'

'Certainly, if that's what you want?'

Kim kept a tight rein on her temper. 'I would prefer it to your subtle hints and insinuations.'

'Well, Kim, you asked for this, remember,' Ursula smiled with satisfaction, her voice no longer purring, but cold and harsh. 'Adam was mine before he married you, and I have every intention of recovering what belongs to me.'

'You speak of Adam as though he were a parcel that could be dropped and picked up at will,' Kim remarked with disgust. 'What makes you think he wants to be recovered like lost property?'

'Adam made a grave mistake when he married you and, if he hasn't realised it yet, he soon will,' Ursula continued coolly and with a confidence that was sickening. 'You obviously have very little experience of men, my dear. They're peculiar creatures, and Adam is no exception. They thrive on mental, as well as physical stimulation, and while I have no doubt that you can offer a certain amount of physical stimulation, can you stimulate him mentally?' She smiled belligerently while Kim maintained a stony silence. 'There's something else you may not know about Adam. He always had an eye for a beautiful woman. I must admit that recently you've done something to make yourself reasonably attractive, but what do you think his reaction will be if he should regain his sight at some future date?'

'I don't frighten easily and, as far as my looks are concerned, I have no illusions.' Ursula had laid an unkind finger on a tender spot that made Kim wince inwardly, but she was determined not to show how much that statement had affected her. 'If Adam should ever wish for a divorce, he has only to say so.'

'That's very wise of you, my dear.'

Kim stared at Ursula for some time. The woman's audacity was beyond her comprehension, while at the same time it was almost laughable. It made no difference to Ursula that Adam was married to someone else. She wanted him, and she had made it quite plain that she was going to get him. All Kim could do was silently wish her luck.

'You seem very sure of your ability to win him back, Ursula?'

'I am.' She graciously disentangled her curvaceous figure from the dresser and came closer to Kim, confidence putting the purr back in her voice. 'I've known Adam for some years . . . intimately.'

Kim's glance sharpened. 'And what, exactly, is that supposed to mean?'

'Don't be obtuse, my dear. When a man and a

woman have known each other for as long as Adam and I have, their relationship is bound to become intimate at some stage.' She smiled with acute satisfaction as Kim's eyes widened in her pale face. 'Does this shock you?'

'Yes, it does,' Kim managed through stiff lips, cringing inwardly from the blow Ursula had delivered, but she lifted her chin proudly and faced her unflinchingly. 'I'm old-fashioned enough to believe that a woman should be married to a man before she gives herself so completely.'

Ursula laughed bitingly. 'Oh, my dear Kim, how puritanical you sound, and how innocent! This is the twentieth century we're living in, and almost everything is permissible these days.'

'So it seems,' Kim replied woodenly, brushing past her with the tray, and not quite knowing how she would get through the rest of the evening.

It was not until after Bill and Ursula had left that Kim allowed herself to think, and the delayed realisation was much worse than the initial shock. She lingered in the bathroom much longer than usual that night, praying that Adam would be asleep when she emerged. If he were to touch her tonight, she would scream, she thought with frantic misery as the tears ran unheeded down her cheeks. A shuddering sigh escaped her as she finally dashed the tears away with an impatience she seldom displayed. She frowned suddenly. What was it exactly that Ursula had said?

'When a man and a woman have known each other for as long as Adam and I have, their relationship is bound to become intimate at some stage.'

Kim winced anew, every part of her being rejecting

the implication in Ursula's statement, yet finding it impossible to evade the truth. Ursula had been Adam's mistress! Innocent as she was, she knew what that meant, and it filled her with revulsion to think that Ursula could have admitted it without a trace of shame. Kim towelled herself vigorously until her skin glowed, anger lending strength to her movements. She hated Ursula, and she hated Adam! He must have been more blind before the accident than he was now, if he could have found such a cold, calculating woman attractive enough to . . .!

She drew her breath in sharply and clipped her thoughts severely. 'This won't do,' she decided rationally. 'Despite everything, I love Adam and, if I want our marriage to continue, I'll have to stop torturing myself.'

Brave words; brave decision. Nevertheless, her bravado deserted her as she left the bathroom and found Adam lying wide awake, and waiting for her.

'What were you and Ursula discussing in the kitchen this evening?' he asked as she slipped gingerly into bed beside him.

'Nothing in particular,' she replied with thudding heart. 'Why?'

'Oh, nothing,' he murmured thoughtfully. 'You seemed to be rather preoccupied and silent afterwards. Did she say anything to upset you?'

'Tell him! Tell him!' a little voice urged, but Kim shrank away from the idea. 'No,' she lied uncomfortably. 'We merely . . . talked.'

'I see.'

He stretched out an arm and flooded the room in darkness. Kim's heart beat suffocatingly fast in her throat. 'Don't touch me!' her soul cried in anguish, yet when his arm slipped about her waist to draw her closer she remained silent and tense. Initially, her lips were unresponsive beneath his, but when he pushed the strap of her nightgown off her shoulder with gentle fingers and slid his hand caressingly over her breast, Kim could not suppress the quiver of delight that went through her.

As if sensing a certain reluctance and withdrawal in her responses, Adam made love to her with a touch of deliberation that finally obliterated everything except the ecstatic pleasure she was experiencing at that moment. Ursula no longer existed. Nothing existed beyond Adam and herself, and that moment in time.

Despite Kim's efforts to prevent Ursula's remarks from placing a barrier between Adam and herself, an unavoidable tension sprang up between them occasionally which resulted in Kim withdrawing into herself. Kim referred to these occasions silently as bouts of morbid self-pity, and Ursula's constant presence in their daily lives was a continual reminder to Kim of the things she would rather forget. It was a devilish situation she could do absolutely nothing about. It was imperative that Ursula worked closely with Adam, and Kim knew better than to interfere in matters of such vital importance, but if Ursula had to feature so prominently in their lives for the duration of their marriage, then Kim could only predict disaster.

Towards the middle of January, Kim telephoned Bill at work one morning and invited him to dinner one evening during that same week. It would be her birthday, she explained.

'Don't mention this to Adam,' she pleaded. 'I don't want a fuss made, but I would like to have you here as my guest. Ursula will naturally be here as well,' she added ruefully.

'That woman is like an irritating thorn in the side,' Bill acknowledged. 'I often regret making the suggestion that she should work with Adam, but the suggestion was made before I knew about you.'

He sounded so downcast that Kim was forced to pass it off lightly. 'Don't let it upset you, Bill. I'm sure we shall survive.'

Optimistic words, Kim thought, grimacing at herself as she replaced the receiver. 'We shall survive,' she had said, as though Ursula were a disease for which there was no antidote.

Kim spent a fair amount of time on that special day, planning the dinner for that evening, as well as deciding what to wear. Adam, she knew, would not be working late, for they were past the stage where this was necessary. As the time approached for Adam to arrive from the Institute, Kim slipped into a cream-coloured, full-length chiffon dress, with the finest lace at her throat. A swift glance in the mirror told her that she had selected wisely, for the dress gave her an air of sophistication and confidence she was sadly lacking.

On a magnificently carved stinkwood table against the wall of the living-room stood a vase of bright yellow roses which had arrived early that morning from Bill. Kim smiled with amusement as she touched the delicate blooms and inhaled their fragrance. On the accompanying card Bill had written: 'It isn't very often that I send flowers to a lovely lady. I have my reputation as a bachelor to think of, so this had better be a very happy birthday for you, Kim.'

Strangely enough, Bill was the first to arrive, a bottle of champagne tucked under his arm. 'Hello, and how's my girl?'

'Just fine, thank you, Bill,' she replied, offering her cheek for his kiss and leading the way into the living-room, 'and thank you for the roses. They're beautiful, and I've just been admiring them once more.'

'It was my pleasure,' Bill replied promptly, depositing the champagne and glancing about expectantly. 'Adam not home yet?'

'No, but I'm expecting him at any moment.'

'He *is* coming home early this evening, isn't he?'

'I'm sure he is.' Kim bit her lip nervously and frowned. 'He usually telephones early in the afternoon if he can't make it.'

'Well, that's all right, then.'

What would she do if Adam did not come home in time for dinner? she wondered anxiously. She had not expected him to remember her birthday, but it would be a disappointment if something prevented him at the last minute from coming home early.

Kim gestured nervously. 'Shall I pour you something to drink?'

'I'll help myself,' Bill said swiftly, going across to the cabinet. 'Sherry for you?'

'Yes, please.'

Kim listened with half an ear to Bill's amusing chatter as the minutes sped by while they sat sipping their drinks. It was almost seven-thirty. Why was Adam not here? What was keeping him so late? Why did he not telephone?

Kim could no longer contain her agitation as she

143

interrupted Bill. 'I hope nothing has happened.'

'Now don't start imagining things. He'll most probably come walking through that door at any moment now,' he tried to pacify her, without success. At that moment the telephone rang shrilly in the study and Kim jumped nervously. Bill glanced at her with swift concern. 'Shall I take it?'

She shook her head and rose shakily to her feet. 'No, I'll . . . answer it.'

Her fingers tightened convulsively on the receiver as Ursula's voice came over the line. 'Adam asked me to let you know that he'll be home late. Something unforeseen happened that can't be left for tomorrow.'

'I—I see.' Kim swallowed down her disappointment. She could hear Ursula place her hand over the mouthpiece as she spoke to someone at the other end before removing her hand once more.

'Adam says don't keep him any dinner. He'll have a snack sent up from the canteen.'

'Can I speak to him?' Kim asked with swift urgency.

'I'm afraid not, Kim. He's just left the office with one of the chaps from the laboratory.'

Kim's shoulders sagged, her hopes plummeting to the ground. 'Very well, then. Goodbye.'

'Something wrong?' Bill asked anxiously as she entered the living-room, her disappointment hanging like a cloak about her.

'Adam won't be home for dinner after all,' she told him woodenly. 'Something occurred which needs their immediate attention.'

Bill scowled momentarily as he glanced at the droop of her shoulders. 'Well, we can't allow an excellent dinner to go to waste, can we?'

Kim raised her sombre glance and pulled herself together instantly. 'You're right, we can't.'

'Good!' he grinned, rubbing his hands together in characteristic fashion. 'You get the dinner on the table while I collect two glasses and open the bottle of champagne.'

Kim removed the excess silver from the table and served dinner for two. Her appetite had deserted her, but Bill showed no sign of being put off his food. They toasted each other with champagne and talked, but Kim found it increasingly difficult to pretend that nothing had happened. More than anything else in the world she had wanted Adam there with her, but his work was more important than his wife's birthday, she thought unreasonably.

'I think it's a rotten bad show,' Bill remarked eventually as she served coffee, and Kim's armour crumpled.

'Oh, Bill, I'm sorry. I don't know what I would have done without you, but it's my fault really. I should have told Adam that I was planning something like this, but I . . .'

'Had no way of knowing that things would go wrong at work,' he finished for her sympathetically. 'You also hoped that he would remember it was his wife's birthday without being told.'

Kim nodded, catching a trembling lower lip between her teeth. 'It was silly of me, I suppose.'

'Not at all,' he insisted with swift understanding. 'Having three sisters made me realise at an early age that women like their husbands to remember little things such as birthdays and anniversaries.'

'I shouldn't really have expected Adam to remember. He's been so busy.'

Kim rose from her chair and walked stiffly away from him as tears threatened to choke her, but Bill followed her and turned her about to face him. 'Your loyalty and understanding is not entirely misplaced, Kim. He mentioned a few days ago that it would be your birthday today. I can only think that pressure of work——'

'Please, Bill,' she interrupted him, resting her head against his shoulder as his arms went about her comfortingly. 'Don't say anything further. I'm ashamed of myself, although I'm naturally disappointed.'

Kim dried her tears quickly and went through to the bedroom to repair the damage to her make-up. When she returned to the living-room, Bill had poured her a small sherry as well as pouring a stiff whisky for himself, then they settled down to wait for Adam.

'I have no right to keep you here so late,' she protested apologetically.

'I'm not leaving until Adam has arrived,' Bill declared firmly, and nothing Kim could say would dissuade him.

It was after ten when they heard the fumbling of a key in the lock. 'Kim, forgive me for being so late, my dear,' Adam apologised profusely as he entered with Ursula close behind him. He stopped suddenly and turned his head in a listening attitude, sniffing the air lightly. 'Bill? Are you here?'

'Yes, I am.'

Kim stood immobile as she saw the hardening of Adam's jaw. It had angered him to find her alone with Bill, and his voice was tinged with sarcasm when he finally spoke.

'Quite a welcoming party, it seems.'

'By the look of things, that's exactly what's been

happening,' Ursula remarked, coming up beside him and slipping her arm through his with a look of triumph on her face. 'A table set for two, candlelight, and empty champagne glasses, as well as an enormous bouquet of yellow roses in a place of honour in the living-room.'

Bill moved then, his manner threatening as he approached Adam. 'As a matter of fact, we did have a celebration dinner. It happens to be Kim's birthday.'

Adam's face went white beneath his tan as he assimilated the shock. 'Oh, lord! I forgot about it completely.' He extricated himself rather impatiently from Ursula's hold as he moved towards Kim, who remained statue-like, a few feet away from him. 'Kim, forgive me?'

Bill glanced from one to the other and cleared his throat. 'Yes . . . well, if you'll excuse me, I'll be off. Coming, Ursula?' he asked, glancing at Ursula's now surly face.

'Well, I——' she began reluctantly, but Bill took her firmly by the arm and almost dragged her physically through the front door, closing it firmly behind them.

Kim faced Adam in the uncomfortable silence that followed Bill and Ursula's departure. She should lash out at him in anger and disappointment, she told herself, but at that moment she was not quite sure how she felt. Adam's apparent distress at having forgotten her birthday had somehow robbed her of the desire to underline the fact with a display of temper.

'Kim?' He extended his hands towards her, but she stubbornly refused to go forward and take them. 'Have I done the unforgivable?'

'I didn't really expect you to remember.'

'But I *did*,' he insisted, coming towards her with a measure of uncertainty. 'It was only when things started erupting at work that it slipped my mind.'

'It doesn't matter.'

'It *does* matter,' he argued harshly, reaching out for her and gripping her arms so tightly that she winced as he drew her against him. 'It matters very much.'

'Oh, Adam . . .'

She placed her cheek against the rough material of his jacket, and stood for a moment in the circle of his arms until he drew her towards the study. She stood aside curiously as he searched the drawer of his desk, taking from it a small, neatly wrapped parcel which he handed to her.

'It's for you,' he grinned apologetically. 'I told Bill what I wanted and he bought it for me last week.'

Kim's throat tightened as she removed the wrapping with trembling fingers. 'It's an emerald brooch,' she said at last, staring down at it in fascination where it lay against the cushioned interior of the small box.

'Emeralds to match your eyes,' he explained, taking her face between his hands and lowering his head to capture her lips in a lingering fashion. 'Happy birthday, Kim.'

'Oh, Adam!' Her voice broke, tears choking back the words of appreciation for his gift.

Adam's thumbs explored her cheeks. 'You're crying.'

'It's such a beautiful brooch,' she laughed tearfully at his amazement, flinging her arms about his waist and burying her face against him. 'Thank you, Adam. Thank you for not forgetting entirely.'

'Kim, my darling, I feel terrible about it.'

Kim's heart jolted violently. *'My darling.'* Adam had never called her that before. Was it merely because he was distressed?

'I'm free this week-end,' he continued, unaware that he had said something unusual. 'Shall we go to the cottage at Heron's Bay?'

Kim raised her head in surprise. 'Are you truly free? You're not just saying this because you feel you have to?'

'No, my darling, I'm not just saying this because I feel I have to. I need the peace and quiet of Heron's Bay.'

'*My darling*.' He had said it again, and her treacherous pulse quickened alarmingly.

'Would you like to go?' Adam persisted, frowning down at her, and she lost herself in his blue gaze.

'Oh, yes, Adam,' came her enthusiastic reply. 'Yes, I would like to go very much.'

'That's settled, then,' he said briefly, dropping a kiss on her silky head. 'If you pick me up at work early Friday afternoon, then we can drive directly to Heron's Bay.'

Happiness surged through her like a melting warmth as she pressed closer to him. 'Oh, Adam, I . . . I think you're wonderful!'

Kim sobered instantly the minute those words were uttered, her joy momentarily forgotten. She had been about to say, I love you. The words had lain ready on her tongue and quivering on her lips before she realised it, and was able to think of a substitute.

'Am I forgiven, then?' Adam asked softly, his hand warm against her cheek.

Kim turned her head slightly and pressed her lips against the palm of his hand. 'How can I help but forgive you when you ask so nicely?'

CHAPTER NINE

KIM and Adam did not arrive at Heron's Bay before nightfall that Friday night, and Kim experienced a familiar stirring of excitement in her veins as she drove up the winding road that led to the cottage. This was where it had all begun, she thought as she approached the cottage and parked the Peugeot in the driveway. This was her place of complete happiness.

'Just smell that sea air, Kim,' said Adam, drawing the air deep into his lungs while they stood for a moment in the moonlit darkness beside the car.

'It's good to be back,' Kim said simply and, for once, Adam did not accuse her of being romantically sentimental.

There was a faint musty smell about the cottage as they entered, and Kim was forced to air the rooms slightly before they finally went to bed. The layer of dust on the furniture would just have to wait until the next day, she decided as she looked tiredly about her. Adam's suggestion that they should spend the week-end at Heron's Bay had come as a wonderful surprise. It was going to be good not to have Ursula around for two whole days, Kim thought ecstatically. Just Adam and herself, with nothing but the sound of the sea, and the mewing of the seagulls overhead to pleasantly disturb the peace.

Kim slept dreamlessly that night until Adam woke her early the following morning. He sat, fully dressed, on the side of the bed with the sun streaming in through the open window, and the slight breeze rippling playfully through the lace curtains.

'Come on, lazybones! The seagulls woke me ages ago.'

Kim glared at him through half closed eyelids and stifled a yawn. 'You sound disgustingly wide awake.'

'I want us to go down to the beach for a swim before the wind comes up, but I want some breakfast first.'

Kim's eyes flew open and she stared up into that lean face with the thick strands of hair that persisted in hanging untidily on his wide brow. 'Food!' she exclaimed, feigning disgust. 'That's all you ever think of.'

'I think about other things as well,' he grinned meaningfully, scooping her up into his arms effortlessly before she could protest, but she held him off with her hands planted firmly against his chest.

'I know that I should have mentioned this before,' she remarked guiltily, changing the subject, 'but what will happen if they should need you urgently at the Institute over the week-end?'

'Ursula will just have to cope on her own.'

'Do you think they might need you?'

Adam's expression was suddenly amused. 'Are you hoping something might spoil our week-end?'

'No, but I should hate to be the cause of keeping you away from something which could be important.'

Adam lowered his head and inhaled the fragrance of her hair while his lips moved deliciously against her neck. 'Nothing is as important as this week-end here with you,' he murmured close to her ear with some urgency.

'Adam, you sometimes say the nicest things,' Kim

sighed happily, sliding her arms about his neck and pressing closer to him.

'What man wouldn't when he's holding such a seductive little bundle in his arms?' he returned mockingly.

'Oh, go away, you hateful man!' Kim laughed exasperatedly, escaping skilfully from the delightful warmth of his arms and making a dash for the bathroom.

Adam was strangely different, Kim thought as she bathed and changed into slacks and a cool blouse. It was almost as if he had recaptured his carefree attitude in the peaceful atmosphere of Heron's Bay. She had to admit that it affected her in the same way as well. The past months in Cape Town could be almost non-existent if she shut her mind to it, and she could almost make herself believe that they had never left this paradise which had been their first home after their marriage. If Adam had not been so tied up at the Institute, they might have been able to escape to this retreat more often, but as it was, they had neglected this cottage drastically.

The sea was beautifully calm when they went down to their private beach for a swim after breakfast. Adam swam with long, powerful strokes beside Kim until she turned on to her back and floated, too exhausted to keep up with him.

'Don't tell me you're tired already,' he laughed at her, treading water when he no longer heard her swimming beside him.

Kim felt herself being lifted by a wave and deposited close enough to Adam to reach out and grab hold of his shoulders. He gave her an unexpected ducking and she came up spluttering.

'Are you trying to drown me?' she gasped as she stared up into his laughing face. A strenuous struggle followed as she tried to pay him back in the same manner, but she eventually collapsed against him, laughing helplessly as her efforts failed.

Just at that moment a wave broke over them catching them off balance, and they both went down to emerge, coughing and spluttering amid their laughter, and close enough to the beach to wade out.

'Let's dry out in the sun,' Kim suggested, wringing out her wet hair as she regained her breath.

'Not a bad suggestion,' Adam agreed, still coughing as he took her arm and dragged her out with him on to the warm, white sand.

They towelled themselves dry before spreading out their towels and lying down with the sun beating down on them. Kim turned over on to her stomach and buried her face in her arms, and for some time she was aware only of a pleasant drowsiness, and a contentment she had not known for some time. Adam was beside her, his arm brushing lightly against hers as he settled himself comfortably, and Kim turned her head slightly to glance at him. His muscular body was tanned a golden-brown, his chest rising and falling gently as he breathed, and his face turned towards the sun. She experienced an overwhelming urge to touch him, but just then his eyes opened and he levered himself up on to one elbow as he faced her.

'Are you happy, Kim?'

Surprised, she raised herself up on to her elbows and stared at him. 'I'm happy if you are, Adam.'

He smiled tolerantly. 'That doesn't exactly answer my question, does it?'

'Adam,' she began, hesitating slightly to assimilate her thoughts, 'have you at any time regretted being married to me?'

'That's a rather odd question!'

'Perhaps, but I would like an honest answer.'

Adam was silent for some time, his expression thoughtful and frighteningly serious. 'Yes, I have occasionally regretted asking you to marry me,' he said at length, and Kim shivered despite the warmth of the sun on her skin. 'I seem to have taken so much from you without giving much in return. I'm aware of your loneliness, Kim, while I spend hours at work, and it's something that troubles me greatly.'

'I don't begrudge you the hours you spend at work while I'm alone at home.' She glanced at him with swift concern. 'You are happy, aren't you, now that you're back at work?'

'Yes, I am . . . although it's most frustrating to have to rely on someone else's eyes all the time. It's stemmed the progress of the project considerably.' He gestured impatiently. 'I don't want to talk about work.'

Kim lowered her head on to her arms once more, and closed her eyes. 'What would you like to talk about?' she asked.

'You.'

'Me?' she asked in astonishment, not daring to raise her head to look at him.

His fingers trailed along the column of her spine and for the first time Kim realised that she was dressed rather scantily in a bikini which she had bought on one of her irrational shopping sprees. His hands rested for a moment in the hollow of her back, then moved upwards again towards her shoulder. Kim remained perfectly still, every nerve vibrant and responding deliriously to his touch.

'Hm . . . you've got sand on your back.'

Kim glanced at him quickly. 'So have you. Shall we have a quick swim to wash off the sand before we go home?'

'Later,' he said firmly, turning her over on to her back and holding her there with the weight of his body. 'I've never kissed you on the beach before, have I?'

He lowered his head, blotting out the sun, and the world spun dizzily about her as her lips came to life beneath the demanding pressure of that hard mouth. His kiss was deliberately sensual, and uncontrollable desire pulsed through her veins. It frightened her, this intense emotion he always roused within her.

'Adam, please! Someone might see us,' she gasped eventually, trying to push him away. But he caught hold of her wrists and pinned her arms against her sides with his strong hands, making her efforts of escape futile.

'Is there a law against a man kissing his wife on the beach?' he asked roughly, trailing his lips across her cheek, and down along the column of her throat to where a pulse throbbed in wild response to his touch.

'No, but . . .'

'Your skin is warm and salty,' he murmured, his lips seeking the mysteriously enticing hollow between her breasts.

'Adam . . . don't!' she gasped pleadingly as her clamouring emotions shook through her slender frame. For some inexplicable reason she did something then which she had always prided herself on being able to control in the past. She lost all power of coherent thought, and whispered brokenly: 'Adam, I—I love you.'

The minute those words were uttered, Kim went cold and rigid with fright. What had she said! Those words had come from a heart so filled with intense love for him that they no longer could be suppressed. She had not intended ever confessing her love, but she could no longer hide it, and she prayed silently for strength to bear the humiliation which was sure to follow.

Adam raised his head slowly, staring down at her as though he could see every delicate contour of her face, and the inevitable cynical twist to his lips was clearly evident as she stared warily up at him. Waiting for the blow to fall.

'Do you, Kim? Do you love me as much as you love that apple pie you're always so fond of baking?'

A searing pain shot through her and she shuddered involuntarily as he released her. 'Let's go and have our last swim, shall we?' she suggested.

The effort to keep her voice casual had almost choked her, and the tears that sprang to her eyes blurred her vision, making her gasp as her body hit the cold water with a suddenness she had not anticipated. Adam swam about energetically while Kim followed him at a leisurely pace. Perhaps it would be as well to adopt Adam's attitude and pretend that she had never uttered those words, she decided eventually, but the rawness in her heart could not be denied.

The vicar, Mr Wilson, arrived unexpectedly that Saturday afternoon. He came trudging up the hill, his bald head glistening in the sun, and obviously out of breath from the unaccustomed exertion.

'I saw the car,' he explained as he joined them for tea in a shady spot of the garden. 'My wife is away visiting the children, and it can get rather lonely in the manse without a nagging woman around. I couldn't believe my eyes when I saw your car up here, and I just had to come and make sure.'

'You're very welcome,' Kim assured him as she handed him his tea.

'I didn't hear your car, sir,' Adam remarked, settling back to light his pipe. 'Did you walk?'

'I did, yes,' their visitor replied with an embarrassed laugh, patting his stomach. 'I needed the exercise and, believe me, it's quite a strenuous walk up the hill.'

Adam nodded briefly, puffing smoke into the air, and Kim wondered uncomfortably just what he was thinking at that moment. Did he resent Mr Wilson's untimely visit, or did it please him to think that their visitor had taken the trouble to call? Kim studied his expression but found it impossible to analyse.

'Have you settled comfortably in Cape Town, Dr Granger?' Mr Wilson asked, draining his cup and mopping his face and neck with a large white handkerchief.

'Yes, I have,' Adam admitted amiably. 'It hasn't been easy, but thanks to my colleagues, I've managed to regain a semblance of normality in my life.' He turned towards Kim and gave her the most brilliant smile that almost took her breath away. 'I must add that, without Kim, none of this would have been possible.'

'Praise from you, Adam, is something quite rare,'

Kim said quietly, a new warmth stealing about her chilled heart. 'Thank you.'

'I must give credit where it's due.'

'Are you staying long?' Mr Wilson interrupted.

'Only until tomorrow,' Adam replied swiftly. 'I'm due back at work on Monday, unfortunately.'

'Pity,' Mr Wilson murmured with regret. 'My wife will be sorry to have missed you, I'm sure.'

'I'm sorry I wasn't able to see her as well,' Kim said ruefully. 'Perhaps when we come again I might have the opportunity to pay her a visit.'

'She would like that,' Mr Wilson nodded, rising to his feet. 'I must leave you again, as I still have a sermon to prepare for tomorrow.'

'Kim will give you a lift down to the village,' Adam said with unexpected concern.

'Oh, no, the walk will do me far more good, I assure you, but thank you for the kind offer.'

'I'll walk a little way with you, then,' Kim insisted, glancing anxiously at Adam's tall figure rising from the chair. 'You don't mind, do you, Adam?'

'Not at all. I'll wait here for you.' He extended his hand towards Mr Wilson and the older man clasped it briefly. 'It was nice meeting you again,' Adam said with surprising sincerity. 'Thank you for the short visit, and pass on my regards to your wife when she returns.'

'I'll do that. Thank you.'

They were some distance from the cottage when Mr Wilson stopped and turned to Kim. 'I must admit I'm glad of this opportunity to speak to you alone,' he said. 'I've been very concerned about you, Kim.'

'There was no need for you to be concerned,' she

said swiftly. 'Adam has been very good to me, and I can assure you we're very happy together.'

Mr Wilson regarded her closely for interminable seconds before speaking. 'I must say that marriage has made you blossom into an extraordinarily attractive young woman, but there is a hint of a shadow in your eyes, Kim, that makes me believe that everything is not as rosy as you would have me believe. Am I right?'

Kim met his steady glance and bit her lip nervously. 'We have our problems like everyone else, I think.'

Mr Wilson gripped her shoulder, the pressure of his fingers reassuring. 'If you ever need someone to talk to, you need only telephone and I'll come to you in the city.'

'You're very kind, but I can't expect you to——'

'I'm serious,' he assured her.

'I know,' Kim nodded, her throat tightening, 'and I appreciate your offer tremendously.'

They said goodbye and Kim stood for some time watching the vicar's progress down the hill. As he reached the first cottages at the bottom of the hill, he turned and, seeing her still standing there, he waved. Kim waved back and retraced her steps slowly to where Adam was waiting for her in the garden. He appeared to be in a strangely pensive mood when she joined him, and it was not long before she knew the reason behind it.

'I've been thinking lately that I should sell the cottage,' he said.

'Oh, no!' Kim exclaimed with rising alarm. 'Adam, you can't sell it! I won't let you!'

'Relax, Kim. I've changed my mind now that we have been here again.' He removed his pipe from his mouth and placed it carefully on the ashtray beside him. 'This cottage may yet serve its purpose.'

Kim drew her breath in sharply and felt an uneasy stirring at the pit of her stomach. 'The way you said that makes it sound rather ominous. It's as if you're planning something unpleasant.'

'You're imagining things,' he laughed suddenly, rising to his feet and reaching for her hand. 'Come on, I'd like to go for a walk along the beach before you make supper.'

Kim allowed herself to be drawn to her feet, but throughout their walk she was conscious of the slow, heavy beat of her heart, almost as if it were beating out a message of impending danger. Danger of what? she wondered irritably, trying to shake off this sudden feeling that something was about to happen—something which could quite easily destroy her marriage.

That night, as she lay in Adam's arms listening to the sounds of the insects in the undergrowth which was almost drowned by the roar of the sea, her thoughts kept returning to this feeling she had developed so suddenly that afternoon. Was their marriage in danger of being destroyed? Would Adam be the destroyer, or would Ursula finally succeed in her objective?

Kim buried her face in Adam's shoulder and prayed that it was nothing more than her imagination playing tricks on her. More than ever before she needed the security and knowledge of Adam's love, but Adam believed that security and love did not exist, and she was incapable of proving him wrong.

After their return to the city, the week-end at Heron's Bay became nothing but a memory Kim could cling to.

160

Adam was instantly swept up in his work, becoming completely engrossed in it. His pensive mood, which she had noticed for the first time that week-end at the cottage, seemed to increase daily until he was totally preoccupied with his own thoughts. He hardly ever spoke to her when he was home, and Kim found herself going to bed alone each night while Adam spent hours sitting alone in his study.

At first she tried to draw him out of his shell but, when it became evident that her efforts merely annoyed him, she left him alone to solve his problems in his own way. This was not an easy decision to make, and as time passed she became more concerned. It was then that she decided to speak to Bill at the first available opportunity, but this was difficult to accomplish when he paid them a visit, for Adam was always present. Finally, out of sheer desperation, Kim telephoned him at work one morning and suggested that they meet in town for lunch. Bill seemed strangely reluctant at first, but finally agreed.

'Bill, something is troubling Adam,' Kim began without preamble when they eventually faced each other across the checkered tablecloth at a secluded restaurant. 'He's been acting strangely ever since we went away for that week-end to Heron's Bay.'

'In what way has he been acting strangely?' Bill asked, lighting a cigarette and glancing at her with narrowed eyes through a haze of smoke.

Kim shrugged helplessly, not knowing quite where to begin. 'Well . . . now that he's home most evenings, he spends hours in the study, just sitting there, or pacing the floor until all hours of the night. When I try to talk to him, he practically ignores me.'

'Perhaps he's just tired,' Bill suggested evasively.

'No . . . no, it's something far more serious than that,' Kim insisted with strong conviction, aware suddenly that Bill was avoiding her eyes for some reason. 'He hasn't said anything to you, has he?'

Bill drew hard on his cigarette, filling his lungs before he blew the smoke forcibly towards the ceiling. 'Adam seldom confides in anyone.'

Kim regarded him closely for a moment, her large green eyes pleading and troubled. 'Whatever it is, Bill, it frightens me.'

He became unusually agitated, she noticed. 'I think you're allowing your imagination to run riot,' he said.

'No, Bill,' she said firmly. 'I know Adam and all his moods. I've always been able to cope with his frustration, his anger, and his irritability at not being able to do the things he used to do. This is something different. It's as if he has erected an invisible barrier between us, and no matter how much I try, I can't reach him.'

Bill knocked the ash off his cigarette with unnecessary concentration. 'Perhaps he's just depressed,' he suggested.

'Perhaps,' Kim agreed helplessly, feeling as though she were talking to a stranger, and not to the man who had become her confidant and her friend during the past months.

Their lunch was served and they ate in silence. Bill knew something, Kim was sure, but for some reason he was not prepared to divulge this information to her. Surely she had a right to know what was causing her husband's strange behaviour? she argued silently, pushing her plate aside eventually when the food began to choke her. It had been a mistake to question Bill, she decided when they finally left the restaurant. She should never have expected him to tell her the truth, and she could barely conceal her disappointment. She had considered him her friend; the one person who would be completely frank with her, but she had been mistaken. His loyalty to Adam had silenced him, and not even his friendship with her would make him divulge whatever it was that Adam wanted concealed.

Kim turned to him as they stood outside on the pavement. 'I'm sorry, Bill,' she said.

'I'm sorry too, Kim,' he said, glancing down at his shoes and confirming her suspicions. 'I shan't tell Adam about our meeting.'

'Thank you.'

Kim's lips were tightly compressed as she hurried to where she had parked the car. If Bill would not confide in her, then she would have to speak to the only person who could tell her the truth—Adam! She had to make him understand that his attitude was disrupting their lives completely; shattering the fragile happiness they shared.

Kim had not intended speaking to Adam so soon after her unsuccessful confrontation with Bill, but when he arrived home that evening and shut himself in his study immediately after dinner, it was just more than she could endure. She sat in the living-room staring at the study door for some time before she could scrape up enough courage to invade his privacy, and it was no surprise to her to find him sitting at his desk with his head in his hands and a look of utter desolation and despair on his face.

She went towards him hesitantly, not certain of the reception she would receive. 'Adam, if there's some-

163

thing troubling you, why don't you tell me about it?' she said.

Adam was on his feet instantly, striding about the room as if he wanted to crush everything beneath his feet. 'Nothing is troubling me.'

'Don't be silly,' she argued, following his futile progress back and forth across the room. 'I'm not a fool, Adam. You hardly ever speak to me lately, and when you do, you're distant and evasive. You spend hours each night here in the study, just sitting, staring, or pacing the floor all night. When you do come to bed, you don't sleep very well either. You toss and turn each night until it's almost time for you to get up.'

'If you're saying that I disturb you at night, then it might be a good idea for me to move into the spare room,' he said harshly.

Kim drew a painful breath. 'Is that what you want, Adam? Is it the fact that you're married to me that's troubling you so much?' The pain which had lodged in her chest seemed immovable. 'Have you tired of me, Adam? Have I finally served my purpose? Is this what you're finding so difficult to decide . . . how to tell me that you want your freedom?'

Adam gestured angrily, the harsh lines in his face more prominent than ever. 'For God's sake, Kim, leave me alone! Stop asking so many questions, and stop jumping to conclusions.'

'I want to help you, Adam.'

'I don't want your help.'

'If you don't want my help, then there must be someone you could go to who *can* help you?'

Adam ceased his furious pacing, and his chest heaved as if it had become an effort to fill his lungs with enough air. 'Kim, you don't know what you're saying,' he said with a strange calmness. 'You don't understand!'

'No, I don't understand. I'm stumbling about in the dark trying to discover the reason for your behaviour, but I don't seem to come anywhere near the solution.' She went to him then, her confidence and determination returning swiftly. She had to make him understand that she was not merely trying to interfere. 'I won't question you again, Adam, but please believe that I only want to help you in any way I possibly can.'

'Kim!' She was caught up against him with a suddenness that took her breath away, a desperate urgency in the strength of his arms as they held her. 'There's no one who can help me, not even you. It's something I have to decide for myself, so . . . bear with me, Kim.'

'Oh, Adam, Adam!' she cried, her voice muffled against the hardness of his chest. 'I vowed that I would do everything in my power to make you happy and contented, but at this moment I feel such a failure.'

His lips found hers, and once again there was that touch of desperation in his kiss that made the fear in her heart something tangible. 'You've made me happier than I have deserved to be, my darling,' he groaned into her hair. 'Don't ever doubt that.'

There was so much more Kim had wanted to say, so many questions that still needed answers, but somehow the words were stilled on her lips. She was no nearer the truth now than she had been before, and it seemed she would have to rely on her patience until Adam saw fit to explain what was on his mind. She could only hope that it would be soon.

Standing there in the circle of his arms was immensely comforting, but it did nothing to obliterate the premonition of danger which was becoming her constant companion.

When Adam finally released her, his face looked haunted and haggard. 'Leave me alone, Kim,' he said, not unkindly. 'I can think better when you're not here with me.'

Kim had no option but to do as he had asked, and she left the study without a word, closing the door firmly behind her. She was more baffled now than she had been before their talk. Could it be that, despite the fact that he had insisted that she had succeeded in making him happy, he *was* actually considering whether to ask her for his freedom? During all the months they had been together, he had never once said that he loved her. 'Nothing is lasting,' he had told her once. Especially not their marriage, he had emphasised, and this had been the uncertain basis of their relationship from the very start, she realised unhappily.

CHAPTER TEN

KIM received an unexpected telephone call from Ursula one morning, and for one heart-stopping moment she thought something had happened to Adam. Ursula reassured her quickly, and asked: 'Could you meet me in town, Kim? There's something important I want to discuss with you.'

Kim tensed instantly, her fingers tightening on the receiver. She could not think of anything that could be important enough to warrant a trip into town, but she nevertheless asked: 'What time?'

'Could we make it twelve-thirty at the Gardens tea-room?'

'That would suit me perfectly, Ursula.'

Kim replaced the receiver and glanced frowningly at her watch. Eleven-thirty. That gave her exactly an hour to change into something more suitable for this appointment with Ursula, and with luck she could be in time for the bus that travelled directly into the city, which would save her the trouble of struggling to find parking in the lunch hour rush.

She could not deny that she was more than curious to know what Ursula had to discuss with her. It had to be something important for her to leave Adam alone at the Institute while she drove into town to meet someone whose existence was irksome to her, Kim thought wryly. Ursula had tried everything in the past to make Kim more aware of the uncertainty of her position. Was this another form of attack, or could the reason for this invitation have some bearing on Adam's attitude during the past weeks? Whatever the reason, Kim thought eventually, she would have to take care that Ursula did not suceed in her mission.

Kim and Ursula arrived almost simultaneously at the tea room. 'Shall we sit here?' Ursula suggested with surprising amiability, selecting a table beneath the shady oaks. 'It's such a lovely day that I shan't even mind the pigeons making a nuisance of themselves. I'm glad you could make it, Kim.'

Ursula was overflowing with confidence and charm, Kim noticed as she sat down opposite her, unable to do anything but admire her crystal clear beauty. She was impeccably dressed in the palest lemon suit that accentuated the golden tan she had acquired during that summer and, as usual, not a hair was out of place on her platinum blonde head. She looked incredibly cool and fresh in the sweltering heat, Kim thought enviously as she became aware of the clamminess of her own body.

'What is it you wanted to see me about?' she asked.

'I suggest that we order something first before we get down to the reason for my asking you to meet me here,' Ursula smiled with infuriating calmness as she gestured to the hovering waitress.

They ordered sandwiches and tea and ate in silence. Kim glanced about her at the people seated at the other tables, and her lips twisted into an involuntary smile of amusement. Amongst all these people, who were chatting animatedly to their companions, she and Ursula must appear decidedly odd as they maintained their uncomfortable silence.

A pigeon settled on the table beside Kim and she fed it the last of her sandwich. She became so engrossed in what she was doing that she almost jumped when Ursula spoke.

'Kim, I know you're not the kind of person to beat about the bush, so I'll be perfectly frank with you,' Ursula said with calm deliberation. 'Why don't you give up? Pack your things and go back to where you came from and leave Adam alone.'

Kim stared at her for several seconds in stunned silence, the pigeon forgotten and left to help himself to the crumbs in her plate. 'Why should I do that?' she asked.

'Can't you see that he desperately wants his freedom?'

Kim's mouth went dry and she swallowed convulsively. 'If Adam wants his freedom, he has only to say so. We've always been perfectly frank with each other in the past, and there's no reason why we shouldn't be now.'

Those scarlet lips twisted derisively. 'Don't be deliberately obtuse, Kim. You know it grieves Adam to swat a fly.'

'You mean that he wants his freedom, but he hasn't the heart to ask me for it?'

'I knew you would finally understand.'

Kim stared unflinchingly into those cold grey eyes. 'This doesn't sound like Adam, but has he actually told you that he wants to be free of me?'

'Not in so many words, my dear, but surely it must be obvious to you that he does? You always profess to know him so well . . . haven't you noticed the change in him lately?'

Kim had to admit to herself that the thought had occurred to her quite often, during these past weeks, that Adam was tired of her and might be wanting his freedom, but she would not give Ursula the satisfaction of knowing this. 'Yes, I have noticed the change in him lately, but I don't frighten easily.'

'Perhaps not, but when you go home, take a good look at yourself in the mirror and ask yourself whether Adam would have asked you to marry him had he not been blind.'

The temptation to slap that look of smug satisfaction from Ursula's face was hastily suppressed, though her anger continued to simmer. 'I don't suppose that it has ever occurred to you that some men might marry a woman for some inner quality which they admire, rather than for her outward beauty?'

Ursula's laughter was like icicles in the hot summer

air. 'Don't fool yourself that this applies to Adam, my dear Kim, and there's not a woman in the world who doesn't possess a certain amount of vanity concerning her outward appearance. Why else did you suddenly spend so much money and effort to make yourself look attractive?' She glanced pointedly at Kim. 'Have you ever wondered what Adam's reaction would be if he should regain his sight?'

Kim's heart lurched violently. 'Adam will never regain his sight, so that question doesn't apply.'

'That's where you are wrong, my dear. Adam is flying to Switzerland on Friday to have the necessary operation to restore his sight. Didn't you know?'

There was a deafening roar in Kim's ears as the blood rushed to her head and then receded to leave her deathly pale. Shock surged though her veins, leaving behind a trail of ice that had a numbing effect on her limbs.

'This can't be true!' she gasped.

'I assure you it is,' Ursula confirmed with the satisfaction that her statement had had the desired effect, 'and the mere fact that he hasn't told you should be enough to prove to you that he no longer considers you important enough to inform you of such an important decision.'

Kim stared hard at the woman sitting opposite her, and suddenly felt an uncontrollable anger hammering for release. 'I don't think I like you, Ursula,' she said with a deadly calm that frightened even herself. 'You're calculatingly cruel and selfish. With a warm and generous nature, combined with your outward beauty, you could have been a wonderful person, but at the moment I can only pity your lack of humanity. I suggest you take a slice out of the advice you gave me so freely. Go home and take a long, hard look at yourself and you might discover that you have nothing but a clever brain, and a beautiful face and figure to offer a man, because a slab of ice has lodged where a warm and compassionate heart ought to be. I ought to hate you, Ursula, but I can only feel sorry for you.' Kim drew a shuddering breath and rose to her feet, aware of two grey eyes which had become leaping flames of hatred. 'Thank you for the invitation to lunch, it was most enlightening.'

A squirrel darted from the undergrowth and scurried across Kim's path as she walked through the avenue of trees, her eyes blinded by a fury that became a searing pain as it reached her heart. Adam should have told her. There was no reason why he could not have confided in her, but instead he had confided in his two colleagues and left the announcement of his intentions for Ursula to play as her trump card.

Kim approached a deserted bench and sat down wearily, her thoughts darting back to the conversation she had had with Ursula. Ursula had insisted that she should give up; that she should pack her things and leave Adam. This would, of course, leave the field free for Ursula to step into the position she so craved. Was this what Ursula had in mind?

'Did she think that she could frighten me to such an extent that I would run off like a scared rabbit?' Kim wondered, subconsciously toying with that very idea. Should she leave Adam and make way for Ursula? It was a tempting thought when she tried to visualise his reaction to her appearance. Would he recoil from her because she did not possess Ursula's beauty?

She sighed and rose to her feet, a new restlessness

forcing her to walk while her thoughts pounded relentlessly through her brain. Was this the reason for Adam's preoccupation lately? Was this what he had meant when he said that no one could help him? Could it be that he found the decision difficult to make? But if, according to Ursula, it was such a certainty that he would regain his sight, why then had it taken him so long to decide? Oh, why had he not told her!

'Adam no longer considers you important enough,' Ursula had said, but somehow Kim could not accept this statement. After everything they had been to each other she could never leave Adam, this she knew now with a certainty that gave her confidence to face whatever the future might hold for her, and neither could she believe that Adam would want her to leave.

Kim walked for what seemed like hours before she finally took a bus back to the flat, but once there she could not bear the thought of coming face to face with Ursula once more when she brought Adam to the door. To see them together might shatter her resolve, and she could end up doing exactly what Ursula had hoped for. The desire to run, before further pain was inflicted, was very strong.

In the café on the promenade Kim ordered a cup of tea and sat staring out to sea, but the calm shimmering beauty of the azure sea on that hot summer's day escaped her. The emotional turmoil within her gave her no peace, and she drank her tea hastily before she stalked towards the beach. She removed her expensive sandals and felt the hot sand beneath her feet, experiencing a ridiculous delight in letting the sand trickle through her toes. One of the life-guards recognised her from her frequent trips to the beach that summer, and he raised his hand in salute, his teeth flashing white against the healthy tan of his skin.

'You didn't come for your regular swim this afternoon,' he remarked almost petulantly, his muscular shoulders swinging slightly as he came towards her.

Kim stared up into his handsome face, with the fair hair bleached several shades whiter by the sun, and felt some of the tension leave her. 'I had something to do in town,' she explained briefly.

He nodded, his glance sweeping over her appreciatively before he rejoined his friends. 'See you tomorrow, then.'

'Perhaps,' Kim murmured absently, but he was too far to hear. Life was suddenly so incredibly uncertain that to plan something for tomorrow had become almost impossible. She could not even be sure that there was a place for her in Adam's future.

Dusk was approaching rapidly when Kim stepped out of the lift and approached the entrance to their penthouse. She was tired and hot, and justifiably wary of what would undoubtedly follow. She was determined to get the truth from Adam, no matter what the consequences and, until then, she would cling to her frail hopes as though her very life depended on it.

'Kim, is that you?'

She closed the door behind her as Adam approached, and steeled herself unconsciously. 'Yes, I . . . went for a long walk and I'm afraid I . . . forgot the time.' It was a lame excuse, she admonished herself guiltily. 'I'm sorry.'

Adam's frown deepened. 'You've never been out this late before. I was beginning to think something had happened to you.'

'I had some thinking to do.' She stood before him, trembling and nervous, and aware of a certain impatience vibrating through him. Those sightless blue eyes seemed to search her soul, and an involuntary quiver went through her, making her words come out in a breathless rush. 'Adam, I have something important I want to discuss with you.'

'Yes, yes . . .' he said quickly, drawing her impatiently towards the kitchen, 'but it can wait until you've made us something to eat. Discussions on an empty stomach invariably leave me limp.'

Kim did not have the strength to argue and tied an apron about her waist before she set to work. Having to delay their talk was a drain on her confidence and, by the time they had finished their silent meal, she was not so sure that she could remember her well-rehearsed speech. When she eventually emerged from the kitchen, after doing the dishes, she found Adam slouched in a chair, smoking his pipe, and looking as though he had not a care in the world.

She stood and observed him intently for some time, her love for him like a painful weight in her chest that brought a lump to her throat.

'Is it true, Adam?' she whispered.

'Is what true?' he grunted. 'Don't speak in riddles, Kim, it's not like you at all.'

His impatience with her brought a restriction to her throat and she was forced to swallow convulsively. 'Is it true that you're flying to Switzerland at the end of the week to have an eye operation?'

Adam's face clouded as he removed his pipe from his mouth. 'Who told you this?'

'Ursula.'

'I should have known,' he muttered, his lips drawn into a thin line of disapproval. 'It so happens that I'm booked on a flight for Zurich on Friday, but I hadn't quite made up my mind to go until this morning. I was going to tell you this evening, but it seems Ursula has saved me the trouble.'

Fear licked at her heart. 'Is it . . . dangerous?'

'Any flight has an element of danger these days.'

'I wasn't talking about that!'

'I know,' he laughed briefly at her display of agitation. 'Yes, it is dangerous. I shall either regain my sight, or suffer severe brain damage if the operation fails—in which case I shall become no more than a living vegetable which should, by rights, be considered dead.'

'Don't!' Kim buried her face in her hands as the cry was wrenched from her. His carelessly spoken declaration had scraped along sensitive nerves, leaving her raw and shattered.

'You want the truth, don't you?' he asked quietly.

'Yes,' she murmured huskily, her hands falling limply to her sides. 'Do you have to go? Do you have to have the operation?'

Those heavy eyebrows rose sharply. 'Strictly speaking . . . no.'

'Then *why*?' she begged, her voice filled with the anguish she was going through. 'Why risk your life to have this operation which can offer no guarantee of success?'

Adam laid his pipe aside and rose to his feet. 'Kim, listen to me, and listen carefully, because I shan't repeat the performance.' His hands caught at her shoulders, his fingers biting into the soft flesh. 'There is a chance . . . a very slight chance . . . that I may be able to see again, and I'm going to take it. If I don't take the chance, it could mean my inevitable death, and the thought of having someone like Ursula around to clutter up the time left to me horrifies me. She's the kind of woman who can't work closely with a man without trying to derive something personal out of it.'

Kim's heart leapt and every nerve tingled hopefully as she raised her glance to search his face. 'I thought you liked Ursula.'

'I did like her . . . once.' His mouth softened slightly. 'That was before I met you.'

Kim pressed her face against his shoulder, the warmth of his body penetrating the expensive silk of his shirt. 'Was she your . . . mistress?'

'Very nearly,' he admitted ruefully. 'She's very beautiful, and when a woman continually puts temptation in a man's way, he would have to be very strong-willed not to accept what she was offering.'

'Did you?' She held her breath.

'I told you—nearly—but I regretted it afterwards.'

The upsurge of joy that swept through her was too much to bear and she threw her arms about him, clinging to him in a sort of wild desperation. 'Oh, Adam, my darling, I know this is an unreasonable request, but don't have this operation. I can't bear the thought of losing you. Not now . . . not yet!'

Adam's hand was warm against her cheek before he raised her face to his. 'Kim, I so desperately want to see you.'

'You'll be disappointed, I'm not——'

'I love you, Kim.'

The room tilted crazily about her as she stared up at

him in utter disbelief, the heavy beat of her heart pounding against her eardrums.

'What—what did you say?' she stammered in no more than a whisper, every fibre of her being unconsciously pleading for confirmation.

'You heard me, and I'm not repeating myself.'

So he was not so sceptical and cynical about love after all, she thought, slightly delirious with happiness. 'I thought that I would never hear you speak those words.'

'I mocked you once when you said you loved me. Have I destroyed that love?' he asked with a touch of anxiety that filled her heart with a pulsating warmth.

'Adam, my most beloved, I've loved you for so long, but I didn't dare tell you for fear of being laughed at . . . except once, when it slipped out accidentally,' she added mischievously just before his lips stilled whatever else she might have wanted to say. For the first time Kim held nothing back, and her soul soared to meet his through lips that moved urgently beneath his own. It seemed a long time before Adam raised his head to bury his face in a handful of her silky hair and, even then, neither of them could speak for a length of time. But it was Kim who timidly broke the almost reverent silence between them. 'May I fly to Switzerland with you?'

'No.' He raised his head sharply and held her a little away from him, the determined set of his chin speaking for itself.

'But, Adam,' she pleaded softly, 'my place is with you, and I want to go very much.'

'If the operation is a success, I don't want to see you for the first time in the clinical atmosphere of the hospital. While I'm there, I want to think of you at

Heron's Bay where you'll awake each morning to the mewing of the seagulls.' He drew her into his warm embrace, displaying a sentimentality she had not suspected he possessed. 'Will you wait there for me, my darling?'

Kim considered this for a moment, torn between her longing to accompany him, and the desire to please him. Then she relented. 'Yes, I'll wait for you at the cottage, if you insist.' Her green eyes darkened suddenly with anxiety. 'What if the operation isn't a success?'

He lowered his head and kissed her briefly on the lips. 'Then you'll be amongst friends, and I have no doubt that they'll take care of you.'

'Are you going alone?' she asked.

Adam released her then and walked towards the table beside his chair where he had left his pipe, and he lit it carefully before replying. 'Bill is coming with me. The Institute has given him special leave for this purpose, so he'll be keeping you posted from time to time.'

Fear spread its icy fingers along her veins, tightening the nerves at the pit of her stomach into an aching knot. 'Adam, I'm afraid,' she whispered.

He turned towards her then, and she realised for the first time what an effort it must have been for him to keep a tight rein on his own emotions. 'What has happened to your faith and your courage, my Kim?'

Kim hung her head in shame at his soft spoken query. 'Forgive me my weakness at this moment, Adam, but . . .' Tears stung her eyelids and finally overflowed to trickle unheeded down her cheeks as she flung herself into his arms with a strangled sob. 'Oh, my darling, I love you so much!'

There was no need for Adam to return to the Institute, and they spent the last few days together before his departure. Ursula called only once during this time, but it was obvious to Kim that she was well aware of the fact that she had lost. She mentioned something about accepting a transfer to Johannesburg, but neither Adam nor Kim were particularly interested. Ursula finally left and they knew somehow that the would not see her again.

They carefully avoided mentioning the reason for Adam's trip to Switzerland, but Kim's agonising thoughts and fears were predominant in every moment of happiness they shared. It was like a sombre cloak she could not shed. What would she do if the operation turned out to be a failure? Now that she was sure of his love for the first time, was she going to lose him again?

Kim drove Adam and Bill to the airport that Friday afternoon which she had dreaded all week, but it was the most unbearable journey she had ever experienced. As they waited for their flight to be called, Bill smiled at Kim several times with forced confidence and patted her hand in a fatherly fashion, but there was nothing anyone could do to relieve the burden of anxiety and fear under which she was labouring. Adam's hand found hers and, although the pressure of his fingers was reassuring, she knew that this moment of parting was just as difficult for him.

Kim jumped nervously when their flight number was called. It was not too late, she thought wildly. Adam could still change his mind! But one glance at his sombre face told her how futile her hopes were. For Adam there was no turning back. It had taken him a considerable time to make this decision, and nothing would dissuade him at this crucial moment.

'We have to go,' Bill reminded them almost apologetically as they rose to their feet.

Kim found herself clutched almost violently against Adam's chest, his arms like agonising steel bands about her. 'Whatever happens, my darling, I want you to believe that you made life worthwhile and, if I don't return, find happiness, Kim. Find the happiness you deserve.'

'You are my happiness, Adam,' she said simply, not quite able to control the tremor in her voice.

Adam nodded briefly as if he understood, and swept her close for the last time as he kissed her hard on the lips.

Was this for the last time? Was this goodbye? Kim wondered frantically as she watched Bill take Adam's arm and lead him away. Was it going to end like this? The pressure of his arms, a brief kiss, and then nothing more? 'Oh, no!' she groaned loudly, not caring about the curious glances of the people milling about her. Adam *had* to live! He was too vital, too alive, to become nothing more than a vegetable. He *must* live!

'Oh, God, please bring him back to me,' she prayed silently as the Boeing rose into the air, and she stood immobile until it was no more than a dot in the sky. 'Please bring back the man I love.'

The cottage at Heron's Bay became a lonely sanctuary for Kim, with memories of happiness shared there with Adam to fill her days and haunt her dreams, while Mr Wilson and his wife became the only two people she could confide in during those weeks of waiting.

The first few days, until after Adam's operation, were downright torture until Bill's telegram arrived to say that Adam had survived the operation, but that there was still some doubt about the restoration of his eyesight. Kim's relief was so great and so intense that she wept in a way she had not done since she was a child. Adam would live! was all she could think of. What did it matter if he still could not see—he would live, and he would be coming back to her.

Bill's weekly telegrams became an unexpected life-line which she clung to desperately and, thirsting for news of Adam, she would read the printed words repeatedly until she knew them from memory. Every nuance of Bill's messages was noted and thrived upon. An unexpected letter from Adam's father told her that he was following Adam's progress just as anxiously as she, and this gave her a measure of comfort to know that she was not alone in this respect.

It was autumn, less than a month away from the anniversary of their first meeting. The autumn roses were making a colourful display in the small garden, thriving on the attention Kim had given them since her arrival. When she was not pottering about in the garden, she spent her days taking long walks, or sitting on the beach for what seemed like hours, just staring out to sea and watching the seagulls circling the fishing vessels expectantly as they approached the primitive harbour.

Waiting! Just waiting! Bill's telegram to say that the operation had been a complete success had lightened her load of anxiety, yet it presented an entirely new problem. She would no longer be an imaginary being to Adam. Those blue eyes would no longer look directly at her, and not see her. What would she see in those eyes? Disappointment?

It seemed that she still had to wait an eternity before the news arrived that Adam was at last returning to South Africa; to Heron's Bay. And Bill, dear faithful Bill, would be bringing him . . . to her!

Consumed with nervous energy, Kim could not remain in the cottage on the day Adam was to arrive. She had no idea what time to expect him, and could only presume that it would be late afternoon.

On the mantelshelf in the lounge stood an enlargement of their wedding photograph, and Kim stared at it several times as she restlessly paced the floor. Adam's eyes looked directly at her from the photograph, and there was that familiar twist to his lips that suggested mockery. With her hand resting on his arm, Kim stood beside him, smiling rather tentatively, uncertain of the future, and of the man beside her.

After a light lunch, Kim could no longer remain between the oppressive walls of the cottage, and she went for a walk, her short, nervous steps leading her to the place where she had met Adam.

She had originally planned to look her best for Adam, but finally decided that he should see her as she really was, comfortable and casual in a pair of slacks, and the fleece-lined jacket she had worn on the day they had met. She sat down on a boulder close to the edge of the cliff, and clasped her hands about her one knee as she stared about her with a feeling of unreality. Just as on the first day they had met, there were storm clouds gathering in the sky. It was, after all, that time of the year when storms often lashed the coast, and even as she sat there the waves came rolling in mercilessly, shooting up a heavy spray of foam as they beat against the rocks below.

The sea was restless, swelling and subsiding at a sickening pace while the wind grew stronger. Kim experienced the same restless quality. What would Adam say? What would he think? Would his disappointment in her appearance mean the end to her dreams of happiness as his wife? So engrossed was she in her disturbing thoughts that she jumped violently when a stone crashed to the ground beside her. She swung round and rose quickly to her feet, dashing her hair from her eyes, to find that she was no longer alone.

'Adam!' she gasped anxiously, his name coming hoarsely through parted lips as she struggled vainly to control her suffocating heartbeats. His complexion was still surprisingly tanned for someone who had spent several weeks in hospital, she noticed absently, her eyes going hungrily over his tall frame and, with the inevitable sunglasses he always wore when out of doors, he looked very much the same . . . and yet, she knew, there was a difference.

The wind whipped his hair across his tanned forehead. 'This is where we met, is it not?'

'Yes,' she managed stiffly, not daring to move. 'I . . . had no idea what time to expect you.'

She stood before him, defenceless and vulnerable without the shield of his blindness for protection. Behind those dark lenses his eyes were frighteningly alive, moving with deliberate slowness from the top of her russet-coloured head down to the comfortable walking shoes on her feet. It was a devastating experience that left her trembling and almost gasping for breath.

'You're more beautiful than I ever imagined, and my imagination certainly ran riot on occasion,' he said slowly, the corners of his mouth lifting in amusement. 'Do I get a welcome, or don't I?'

'Oh, Adam!'

She was in his arms then, tears mingling with her laughter as he showered kisses on her cheeks, her eyes, her nose, and finally her waiting lips.

'Kim . . . my darling . . . my wife,' he kept muttering in a voice that was warm and vibrant. 'The possibility that I could be throwing away everything that I held most dear nearly drove me out of my mind, but I had to take the chance.'

Kim groaned, her arms tightening about him to convey her own desperate anxiety. 'I know, I know. Oh, Adam, I can't tell you what I've been through these past weeks! I can only thank God that you're here with me, and that it's all over.'

'It's not over, my darling. It's just beginning.' He gathered a handful of her hair and buried his face in it as the wind ripped at their clothes, and the first heavy drops of rain began to descend upon them. Adam raised his head reluctantly and glanced up at the sky. 'It seems that even the weather is giving us a second chance.'

'This is where we came in, as they say,' Kim laughed shakily as the rain increased. 'We'd better make a dash for the cottage, or we'll be drenched.'

Hand in hand, and laughing hilariously, they ran towards the cottage, and did not stop until they had slammed the door behind them. Flushed from the unaccustomed exertion, they removed their wet jackets and hung them on the peg against the wall.

Kim sobered suddenly and glanced about her.

'Where's Bill?' she asked.

'He dropped me off and left again immediately.'

A smile of amusement hovered about her lips and sparkled in her eyes. 'How very tactful of him!'

'Very,' Adam agreed solemnly, removing his dark glasses and slipping them into the pocket of his jacket. He turned to face her in the now gloomy entrance hall, and gave her the full benefit of his blue gaze. For several breathtaking seconds she stared into those fascinating eyes, overwhelmed by the alarming knowledge that there was nothing she could ever hide from him in future. As though he still had to rely on his sense of touch, his hands framed her face, his thumbs moving gently across her cheekbones as his eyes looked deep and searchingly into hers.

'I love you, Kim,' he said at last. 'I had to tell you before I left, but I can say it now, knowing that there's a future for us together.'

He lowered his head and kissed her then with an awe-inspiring gentleness that sent her pulse rate soaring.

'Did you know right from the beginning that one day you would have to have the operation?' she asked unsteadily when he finally released her.

'Yes, I knew.'

Understanding was beginning to dawn as Kim followed him into the lounge. 'Is that why you were so cynical about . . . love?'

A rueful expression flitted across his lean face. 'Yes. The original idea was that I didn't want to bind you to me too firmly. You had to be free to pick up the threads of your life if I didn't return.'

The silence that hung between them was pregnant with emotion as she faced him unflinchingly, and with that proud lift to her chin. 'I've never been free from the moment we met, Adam.'

'Oh, my God,' he groaned, raking his fingers through his short, unruly hair. 'You loved me then already?'

Her eyes, large and luminous, gave him his answer as clearly as if she had spoken. 'Nothing would have induced me to marry you had I not loved you,' she whispered, walking straight into his waiting arms.

'Shall I tell you when I first knew that I'd met my fate?' he asked eventually, sliding his lips along her neck.

'When?'

'That very first day when you told me to go ahead and throw myself down the cliff.'

'Oh, Adam!' she laughed in disbelief as she held him off slightly. 'And I always had the feeling that you were still in love with Ursula, and she certainly did her best to confirm my belief.'

'Heaven forbid!' he exclaimed roughly, drawing her against him once more. 'Ursula was intelligent, and she was fun, but one scientist in the family is enough.'

'She's beautiful,' Kim persisted relentlessly, almost as if she could not believe her good fortune that Adam could love her for herself.

'If you go for that kind of beauty that dazzles the eyes and stirs the senses, yes,' Adam teased before his hard mouth claimed hers and created havoc with her pulse rate. Kim slipped her arms about his neck and returned his kisses with a hunger that matched his own. There was no longer any need to hide the love that seemed to be overflowing from a heart that was too full to speak. Adam raised his head then and gazed down into eyes that were dreamy from the passion of his kiss. 'I prefer my women warm, soft, and cuddlesome, with green eyes I could willingly drown in, and lips that are an open invitation to be kissed, and kissed often.'

Kim emerged from her dreamy state of bliss and shuddered involuntarily as she thought of what could so easily have happened. 'My darling, if I'd lost you . . .'

'*Don't*, Kim,' he interrupted swiftly, his arms tightening about her slender frame. 'It's over now, and we're together for always.'

'For always,' she echoed prayer-like as she offered him her lips. There was no longer any need for speculation and uncertainty. Adam was hers, as she was his, until time itself elapsed.

Outside the small cottage the rain came down incessantly, beating against the window-panes and running down in small rivulets, but inside two people sat on the couch with their arms about each other, talking softly in between kisses and quite oblivious of the elements of nature. There was so much still to say, and so much to explore, and time was suddenly more precious than ever before.

Send coupon today for
FREE
Harlequin Presents
Catalog

We'll send you by return mail a complete listing
of all the wonderful Harlequin Presents novels
still in stock.

Here's your chance to catch up on all the
delightful reading you may have missed
because the books are no longer available at
your favorite booksellers.

Fill in this handy order form and mail it today.

Harlequin Reader Service   In Canada:
MPO Box 707,   Stratford, Ontario
Niagara Falls, N.Y. 14302   N5A 6W4

Please send me without obligation my FREE Harlequin
Presents Catalog.

NAME _____
                    (please print)

ADDRESS _____

CITY _____

STATE/PROV. _____ ZIP/POSTAL CODE _____

OFFER EXPIRES DECEMBER 31, 1977   ROM 2101

Did you miss any of these exciting Harlequin Omnibus 3-in-1 volumes?

18 magnificent Omnibus volumes to choose from:

Betty Neels

Betty Neels #3
Tangled Autumn (#1569)
Wish with the Candles (#1593)
Victory for Victoria (#1625)

Violet Winspear

Violet Winspear #5
Raintree Valley (#1555)
Black Douglas (#1580)
The Pagan Island (#1616)

Anne Hampson

Anne Hampson #4
Isle of the Rainbows (#1646)
The Rebel Bride (#1672)
The Plantation Boss (#1678)

Margery Hilton

Margery Hilton
The Whispering Grove (#1501)
Dear Conquistador (#1610)
Frail Sanctuary (#1670)

Rachel Lindsay

Rachel Lindsay
Love and Lucy Granger (#1614)
Moonlight and Magic (#1648)
A Question of Marriage (#1667)

Jane Arbor

Jane Arbor #2
The Feathered Shaft (#1443)
Wildfire Quest (#1582)
The Flower on the Rock (#1665)

Great value in reading at $2.25 per volume

Joyce Dingwell

Joyce Dingwell #3
Red Ginger Blossom (#1633)
Wife to Sim (#1657)
The Pool of Pink Lilies (#1688)

Hilary Wilde

Hilary Wilde
The Golden Maze (#1624)
The Fire of Life (#1642)
The Impossible Dream (#1685)

Flora Kidd

Flora Kidd
If Love Be Love (#1640)
The Cave of the White Rose (#1663)
The Taming of Lisa (#1684)

Lucy Gillen

Lucy Gillen #2
Sweet Kate (#1649)
A Time Remembered (#1669)
Dangerous Stranger (#1683)

Gloria Bevan

Gloria Bevan
Beyond the Ranges (#1459)
Vineyard in a Valley (#1608)
The Frost and the Fire (#1682)

Jane Donnelly

Jane Donnelly
The Mill in the Meadow (#1592)
A Stranger Came (#1660)
The Long Shadow (#1681)

Complete and mail this coupon today!